D0480680
BALL
INTERNATIONAL
FOOTBALL GENIUS

CHAPTER 1

WHAT NEXT – THE WORLDIES?

Hi, everyone. Johnny here! Or, as the *Tissbury Times* described me in their story on Monday 19 May, page 29, middle of the second paragraph (not that I care much about that sort of thing, obviously):

Yes, that's right. Just in case you missed it: I, Johnny N. Ball, became the new Tissbury Tigers manager, and used my amazing football ideas to help lead a team of teenagers (including my big brother, Daniel) all the way to the league title. Not bad for a boy who's still at primary school, eh?

But don't worry, there was no time for me to become a "Puffed-Up Percy", as my Grandpa George would say. (Don't ask me why!) No, just like my hero Paul Porterfield – probably the best manager in the whole wide world – said in his autobiography, "Winning is like a tasty chocolate cake: once you've had one piece, you always

And, apparently, Tigers are the greediest animals of all! You see, just moments after we had beaten Cooperston Cobras to lift the league title for the first time in fifteen years, and before I had even had time to do my special secret handshake with my best friend Tabia, the players were already moving on to talk about our next big match.

"Come on, lads. One more win and we get to go to the Worldies!" boomed Beardy Jake, our gentle giant in defence.

"Yeah! Capdevila, here we come!" added Reggie, our left-wing wizard. "Tigerz on Tour, innit!"

The Worldies, or the "World Youth Championships" as people like my dad still call it, is a legendary tournament where all the top young teams (and managers!) from all over the world come together and compete against each other. It's totally awesome and it takes place every year in Capdevila, a Spanish city famous for three main things:

1) its super-amazing football club
2) its sizzling summer weather with zero rain
3) its beautiful beaches.

Football fun in the Spanish sun – what an adventure it would be!

Although I didn't want to admit it to the Tigers, I was pretty excited about the Worldies too. It was a once-in-a-career opportunity to test ourselves against the best in the business. And if we did well... Just for a nanosecond, I allowed myself to imagine the headline in the *Tissbury Times*: JOHNNY BALL: INTERNATIONAL FOOTBALL GENIUS!

Yes, that sounded super awesome to me.

But while we were now just one game away from qualifying for the Worldies, it wasn't going to be "a piece of cake" (geddit?). Oh no, in the play-offs, we would be taking on the number one team in the entire country, the Kilbracken Kingfishers, or the "Invincibles" as everyone was calling them. Why? Because they had won their league without losing – or drawing – a single game all season:

Position	Team	Played	Won	Drawn	Lost	Total	Goals Scored	Goals Conceded
1	Kilbracken Kingfishers	18	18	0	0	54	162	4

GULP! And as if that wasn't enough for one very young manager to worry about, we also had a PROPERLY MAJOR INJURY PROBLEM. My super-talented big brother, Daniel, had been fouled so badly in the match against the Cobras that he couldn't even take the title-winning penalty. The Worldies play-off was just one week away.

Even with our best team, it was going to be tough to beat the Kingfishers, but without our superstar striker? It seemed almost impossible...

CHAPTER 2

DANIEL'S INJURY DRAMA

On the drive home from Daniel's disastrous match against the Cobras, Mum and Dad tried their best to keep the car nice and positive:

"Don't worry, Danny-doodle. I'm sure it's nothing some rest and magic spray can't sort!"

"Yes. In a few days, you'll be fit and firing again, son."

But they weren't the ones sitting in the back next to Daniel and his really, really injured right leg. It didn't look good AT ALL. His shin was already as swollen as a bulldog with a bee sting, and nearly as purple as the new Tissbury Town away kit. His cool-kid face wasn't fooling me; he was "hurting like

a hotspur", as Grandpa George would say.

Uh-oh. What were we going to do?! If my super-talented big brother couldn't play in the play-offs, the Tigers were in serious trouble. Because, even though we had finally found our football focus and our "teamy" spirit, and we still had Temba, our super-speedy, other best player, things just wouldn't be the same without Daniel, our captain and top goalscorer.

Plus, we "Barnstorming Ball Brothers" were supposed to be taking on the football world TOGETHER. I know Daniel and I argue quite a lot, but we were finally friends again, and it felt like there was no way that I could take the Tigers to the Worldies without him. So, there was only one thing for it: we had to fix Daniel's leg and FAST!

Now, I know what you're probably thinking. If you had a serious injury, you would go straight to the hospital, right? Well, not in my family. My parents like to think they know it all, especially when it comes to football. So, as soon as we got home and Daniel had hobbled through the front door, Dad got to work. First, he grabbed our football first-aid kit and treated Daniel's leg with exactly one minute of magic spray.

(Mum says it's a "secret family recipe" but I tasted it once, and I'm pretty sure it's just tap water.)

"Arghhh!" my brother screamed out in surprise.

"It's working!"

"No, Dad, it's freezing cold!"

"Ohhhh..."

Meanwhile, Mum had rushed over to the big family bookcase and found the shelf marked, "Football Medicine & Physiotherapy". In a flash, she piled the best titles in her arms, until she looked like a librarian trying to break a world record. Surely she wasn't going to read ALL of them?

Oh yes, she was!

"'Two months' rest'? Rubbish. My Danny doesn't have time for that!"

"'ICE'! Of course. Johnny-kins, could you fetch the frozen peas please?"

"'Go to the hospital and get an X-ray'? No, that's no good..."

"'ELEVATION'! Danny, it says here you should keep your leg raised as high as possible... No, I don't think they mean all the way over your head, darling!"

An hour later, after a dose of painkillers ("One for the leg and one for luck, lovey!"), Daniel was fast asleep on the sofa and Mum was down to the final book on her pile: *Alternative Football Remedies* by Will B. Strange. I was expecting her to throw that one aside really quickly. But no; apparently, bad injuries call for bad ideas...

"Johnny, can you check if we have any tins of tuna left in the cupboard?"

"Why?"

"Don't ask questions – just do it!"

For my brother's sake, I was hoping the answer would be no, but, unfortunately, we did have two tins, which I handed over to Mum.

"Lovely. Right, Danny-boo-boo, I'm just going to roll your sock down a bit and spread some tuna on your leg—"

"Hey, what's going on?!" Daniel cried out as a fishy smell hit his nostrils and something slimy landed on his leg.

"Oh great, you're awake! Now, it says here that once you've covered the injured area with tuna, you need to roll the sock back up and then stand on your other leg for an hour. Let me help you—"

"No way, Mum. I ain't up for this MADNESS!"

Daniel had had enough, and I didn't blame him. What we needed was for our parents to calm down and behave normally for once. But no. At that moment, Dad burst back into the room, yelling, "I'VE GOT ANOTHER IDEA!"

Oh dear, that wasn't good news at all. I get amazing football ideas, and so does Grandpa George, but Dad? Not so much...

"So, I was thinking back to *my* awful injury," he began, which seems to be how 99% of his stories begin. "After one minute of magic spray, my coach strapped it up, tight as a new pair of shoes, with lots and lots of tape, until I could hardly feel a thing. Then he said to me, 'Get back out there, Bally. Just play through the pain, you wimp!' Ah, Tony Treadmill – he was a nice man, really..."

"I hear ya, Dad, but that was your ankle, not your shin," Daniel replied while picking bits of tuna off his leg. "Plus, you're talking about ancient timez when footie physios didn't even exist!"

"Hmmm. I suppose things have changed since

then, haven't they...?"

"YES, THEY HAVE!"

That was me who said that, by the way. I couldn't just stand there, staying out of the injury trouble. It was time for me to speak up, and not just as Daniel's brother, but as his Tissbury Tigers manager too. No amount of tuna or tape was going to fix his shin.

"Pleeeeaaaase, Mum. Pleeeeaaaase, Dad. Can we just take him to hospital?" I begged, using my best "I promise I'll never ask for anything ever again" voice.

And it worked. Well, eventually, anyway. After a few "A&E at the weekend – we'll be waiting all night!" grumbles, Dad helped Daniel hobble back out to the car and off we drove. Phew! At least now we would find out my brother's chances of playing in the play-offs, and therefore the Tigers' chances of going all the way to the Worldies.

The wait at A&E was long and tense – thanks to Dad muttering, "I told you!" every five minutes – but finally, it was Daniel's turn to see a doctor.

And the news? Bad. Really, really bad.

"Sorry, young man, but you've fractured your tibia," the woman in the white coat announced with a serious look and a sigh.

Tabia? I thought but didn't say. I had no idea that my best friend was named after part of the human body...

"The tibia is another name for the shin bone," she explained, putting the X-ray up on the screen. "As you'll see here..."

Oh boy. I didn't need to be a top doctor to see the crack in the middle – it was massive. His shin bone looked like a car-park barrier as it lifts up.

"So it's not good news on the football front, I'm afraid. These kind of injuries require a lot of rest."

"How much rest?" Daniel asked anxiously, and I saw him cross his fingers behind his back.

"At least two months. Maybe a bit longer..."

All eight of our shoulders slumped at exactly the same time. We didn't need to look at the family football calendar to know that was waaaay too long.

"On the positive side, it's a good thing you were wearing shin pads because, otherwise, it could have been a whole lot worse."

A whole lot worse?! In that moment, it was hard for us to imagine ANYTHING worse than Daniel going two months without playing football.

"Oh, one final thing: I noticed a few chunks of fish stuck to your son's leg. It just seemed a little … strange. Do you have any idea how they might have got there?"

This time, all eight of our shoulders shrugged at the same time. *Nope, no idea!* The doctor definitely didn't need to know about Mum's weird alternative medicine. We had enough to deal with already. Daniel was out of the play-off and out of the Worldies too, even if I *could* somehow lead the Tigers past the Kingfishers, which now looked like my toughest task yet.

Was I really talented enough to become an international football genius without my brother by my side and in my team? There was only one way to find out…

WING BACKS ON THE COUNTER-ATTACK!

MATCH 1: WORLDIES PLAY-OFF

TISSBURY TIGERS VS KILBRACKEN KINGFISHERS

It was the week before the latest biggest match of our lives, and I should have been preparing my team, planning my tactics and panicking big time. But, instead, I was on the hunt for an extra player. Five days – that's how long we had left before our play-off battle with the Kingfishers, and how long I had to somehow find us a new star striker. But from where? The "Free and Fantastic Footballer" shop?

If only that place existed! I decided to start my search by going to see Mr Crawley, the old Tissbury Tigers manager. Surely someone that friendly would know lots of strikers? But sadly, he was about as useful as a toothbrush to a toucan.

"Sorry, JB. You know me – I'm terrible with names! What about that nice boy with brown hair?"

"Which team does he play for?"

"Erm, err... No, I'm afraid I can't remember that either."

"Never mind. Thanks anyway."

Time for Plan B. Seeing as the Cooperston Cobras were the ones that had injured Daniel in the first place, I thought maybe they might be willing to help us. But it seemed their manager, "Peculiar Pedro" Bolsa, had taken the whole team to Tanzania on a post-season trip to climb Mount Kilimanjaro.

Next, I asked our fierce local rivals, the Rockley Raptors, if we could borrow one of their players, but – surprise, surprise – they said no too. (They had a "special event" that day, apparently...)

OK, so who else could I ask?

Daniel? No, my brother hadn't said a word to anyone since our terrible trip to A&E. He definitely wasn't ready to help find someone to replace him.

Tabia? My best friend was blessed with MAD SKILLZ, but a nine-year-old taking on big, angry teenagers? It didn't sound like one of my most amazing football ideas...

Billy Newland? He was one of the best players at my school, Tissbury Primary, but he was also the biggest bully I knew. No, I would rather miss the Worldies than have to manage him again!

With time running out, I decided to ask the Tigers at training. Did they know anyone – ANYONE! – who could come and play for us?

"Yeah, I've got a mate," said Beardy Jake, sounding very casual about it.

"Great!" burst straight out of my mouth, but there were a few things I needed to find out before I got too carried away:

OK, IS THAT BECAUSE HE'S BRAZILIAN?

NAH, HE'S FROM TISSBURY, OBVS!

FINE, WHAT'S HIS PHONE NUMBER?

DUNNO.

WHERE DOES HE LIVE?

DUNNO. I JUST SEE HIM DOWN THE PARK.

SHOULD I MAYBE LOOK FOR SOMEONE ELSE WE ... KNOW A BIT MORE ABOUT?

NAH, TRUST ME. WHEN HAVE I EVER LET YOU DOWN, J?

I really wasn't sure about this "Si", but what choice did I have? I had to trust Beardy Jake and ... his mysterious mate turned up! OK, so his bike skidded to a stop only five minutes before kick-off and he was still wearing a T-shirt, trackies and trainers. But, hey, the main thing was that he turned up. Hooray! We had eleven players for the play-off!

After a super-quick scramble for kit, Si looked like a proper Tiger and a pretty good player too.

He was big and strong, he could run and he had a powerful left boot – perhaps a little *too* powerful. His first warm-up shot flew so high over the crossbar that the ball got stuck in a tree. Our new star striker? Hmmm. Maybe not...

But we were only moments away from kick-off. Wasn't it too late to start moving the other Tigers around now? "Never tinker with a winning team" – that was Number 3 in Paul Porterfield's "Top 5 Tips for Becoming a Totally Amazing Manager". Arghh! Why did I have to make so many difficult decisions?! As you can tell, I was super-stressing out, but wouldn't you be if you were about to manage the most important match of your life, against the most amazing team in the country, and you had only just met one of your players for the first time?

It might have helped if Daniel had been there on the sidelines to keep me calm, rather than sulking on his own at home. Instead, I had my parents, cheering me on in two different but equally embarrassing ways:

"GO GET 'EM, Johnny-jim-jams!"

"Come on, son. We're one game away from the World Youth Championships!"

Yes, Dad. I know that, duuuuuh! Hand-shield up, football focus on. *Think, Johnny. Think!* In the end, I decided to stick with Si as a striker. He could be our tall target man, flicking the ball on for Temba to sprint after at top speed. Sorted!

Well, it sounded sorted in my head anyway. But out on the pitch? That was a totally different story. Because Kilbracken Kingfishers weren't just brilliant; they were unbelievable. Their players were like robots programmed to football perfection, and if it hadn't been for our keeper Craig's really long, thin ruler legs, we would have been 3–0 down in the first few minutes.

"Well done, son!" Mr Crawley shouted proudly from behind the goal, but it was clear to everyone else watching that the Tigers were in big trouble.

Especially to me. When one team is way better than the other, silly football people often say that it's "men versus boys", but this was more like T. rexes versus tadpoles!

It was only a matter of time before the Kingfishers took the lead and then tore us up into tiny little Tiger pieces. I had to do something to stop that from happening. But what? Where were all my amazing football ideas when I needed them?

Think, Johnny. Think!

As the minutes ticked by, the Tigers dropped deeper and deeper, until all eleven players were inside our penalty area, bravely blocking the goal. We hadn't just "parked the bus" as silly football people sometimes say; no, our bus had fully broken down and it wasn't budging, no matter how hard the Kingfishers pushed. It wasn't fun – or easy – to watch, but at least we weren't losing … yet.

What about your tall target man? you're probably wondering. Well, I admit it – my "Si the striker" plan wasn't working at all. So far, his only header had gone backwards towards our own goal and his only shot had gone so far forwards that it landed on a different pitch.

"Unlucky, Si. Maybe try a short pass next time instead?" I shouted in my best "encouraging coach" voice.

It already seemed like our only chance of winning and making it to the Worldies was to somehow hit the Kingfishers on the counter-attack. But for that to work, we were going to need to get our speediest Tigers sprinting forward again. In my notebook, I made a quick list of our Top 3 fastest footballers:

1. Temba
2. Noah
3. Connor

Hmm. The problem was that two of those three – Noah and Connor – were playing in defence, deeeeeeep in our own half...

TING! LIGHT-BULB MOMENT! I had it – my first amazing idea of the match, and just in time for my Tigers half-time team talk!

You see, twice already that season, we had won

games using a totally awesome tactic I call the "attack of the flying full back". First, Connor had legged it up the left against the Warthogs, then Noah had raced up the right against the Cobras. But it was going to take something even better to beat the Kingfishers, and what's even better than flying full backs? That's right ...

"Flying WING backs!"

At first, the Tigers stared at me like I was speaking a foreign language.

"Wing backs! Come on, guys. You know what wing backs are – they're like full backs but a lot more attacking!"

Still no response. Maybe they were so exhausted that their ears had stopped working. Was that a thing? Just in case it was, I walked around holding up my totally awesome new tactics sheet in front of each and every player like it was a missing-person poster.

"See! That's you there," I said, pointing at their names on the page.

At last, I saw some nods, and I even heard a few murmurs of "Aaah, sick". Brilliant, but what about Si? I really needed him to understand the plan because I was asking him to move all the way from one end of the pitch to the other – from striker to central defence, next to his mate, Beardy Jake. Then with three big guys at the back, our wing backs would have the freedom to fly forward on the counter-attack. Gottit?

"Gotcha, boss. Bang on," mumbled Si.

Team tactics? TICK! Now it was time for Part 2 of my half-time team talk: player positivity. Because of the stressful striker situation, I hadn't had time to boost them up before kick-off. This was my chance to make them feel like champions.

"Tigers, I know you're tired, but that's because you're defending like dragons out there. I'm super proud of every single one of you! Keep going and keep believing in yourselves. Yes, the Kingfishers won their league, but so did you. Remember that and remember this: one more win and we're off to the Worldies. So, I want you to give it everything you've got in this second half. Let's do this!"

"Right, Tigerz, on three," our new captain, Temba, called out from the centre of the team huddle. "1, 2, 3..."

Now, we were ready. Ready for ... WING BACKS ON THE COUNTER-ATTACK!

All we needed now was the ball. It took us about ten minutes, but finally Si used his strength to win it back and then he blasted it forward first time towards Temba, who controlled it beautifully on his boot. Now what?

Wing backs, go, go, GOOOO!

ZOOM ... ZOOM!

With the Kingfishers totally dominating the match, their manager had only left two defenders back. *Biiig mistake!* Because, as Temba turned with the ball, there was Connor legging it up the left and there was Noah racing up the right. Three versus two – our opponents were outnumbered!

"Go on, go on!" I muttered to myself as Temba took the ball forward at top speed. When a Kingfisher finally tried to tackle him, he faked a pass to Connor but slipped it to Noah instead, who passed it straight back. ONE-TWO! The Kingfisher defenders just stood there, dazed and a little dizzy, as Temba dribbled into the penalty area and fired a fierce, low shot into the bottom corner.

GOOOOOOOOOOOAAAAAAAAAAALLLLLLLL!

Woah, what a wing-back counter-attack! My idea had worked, and the Tigers were winning! I gave the air a little fist pump but kept my major celebrations on the inside for now. We weren't through to the Worldies yet.

After that one amazing counter-attack, the Tiger bus broke down again. Our back three became a back five, and our attackers formed a second line of defence in front of them, saying, "You shall not score, Kingfishers!"

And they didn't. They tried again and again, but there was no way through our determined defence. At last, the final whistle blew and our nervous wait was over. We had done it – Mission Almost Impossible completed. Despite Daniel's injury, the Tissbury Tigers were on their way to the Worldies!

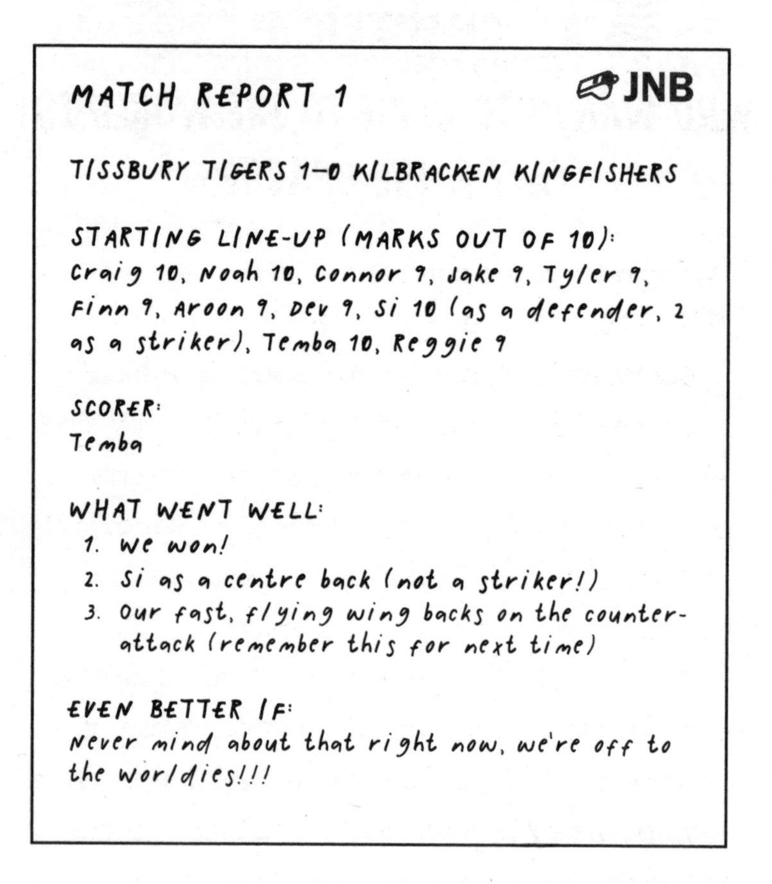

MATCH REPORT 1 JNB

TISSBURY TIGERS 1–0 KILBRACKEN KINGFISHERS

STARTING LINE-UP (MARKS OUT OF 10):
Craig 10, Noah 10, Connor 9, Jake 9, Tyler 9, Finn 9, Aroon 9, Dev 9, Si 10 (as a defender, 2 as a striker), Temba 10, Reggie 9

SCORER:
Temba

WHAT WENT WELL:
1. We won!
2. Si as a centre back (not a striker!)
3. Our fast, flying wing backs on the counter-attack (remember this for next time)

EVEN BETTER IF:
Never mind about that right now, we're off to the Worldies!!!

CHAPTER 4

WHO WANTS TO COME TO THE WORLDIES? PART 1: THE COACHES

"Worldies, here we come!"

"TIGERZ, TIGERZ, TIGERZ!"

Our team celebrations went on and on for hours and when I got home that night, I was still way too excited to sleep. Instead, my brain took me on a virtual tour of Capdevila – the sea, the sights and, of course, the football stadium. Yes, it was really happening – we were going to the Worldies!

The next morning, however, it was back to reality and back to school. I was still only half awake as I stumbled out of the front door with a triangle of toast between my teeth, so it was a bit of a shock to find my buzzing best friend waiting for me.

"Here, he comes: the Tiger KING!" Tabia clapped and cheered at a volume that hurt my sleepy head. "I've said it before but I'll say it again – you, Johnny Ball, are a football genius!"

Like all best best friends, Tabia had believed in me and my amazing ideas from the very beginning – waaay before the Tigers and before everybody else at Tissbury Primary too. We were a team, which meant that my success was also her success, especially when there was a summer holiday involved.

"When are we off to the Worldies then?" Tabia asked eagerly, before I'd even finished eating my toast.

"WE?" I mumbled with my mouth full. (I know, silly question ... and sorry, bad manners too.)

"Yeah, WE! What, you think I'm staying here in Tissbury while you and your team are having the time of your lives in Spain? No chance, ***CRAB-CLAWS!*** Plus, you know how much I love Capdevila – they're my dream club!"

It takes a super-brave person to say no to Tabia Haddad, and as you probably know by now, that's not me.

Besides, if I was going on a big international adventure to manage the Tigers against the best youth teams in the world, then I wanted my best friend by my side.

"Welcome to the team, Tabs!" I said with a smile. "I'll get my mum to speak to your mum."

Talking of mums, if the Tigers were going on tour, we were going to need ... GROWN-UPS. Yes, proper grown-ups with money and jobs, not just teenagers like Beardy Jake who look old because they've got a beard. You see, although nine-year-olds like me are allowed to manage football teams, sadly, we're not allowed to travel the world without adults around to "look after" us.

I know, I know. Being a kid sucks sometimes. But then I remembered the super-wise words of Paul Porterfield in Number 5 of his "Top 5 Tips for Becoming a Totally Amazing Manager": "No manager is an island. To achieve great things, you must work together with those around you." Really, did I have to?

I guess it could be useful to have some coaches there to help me, I thought, picturing Paul Porterfield with his brilliant team of brainy football people behind him. OK, so I didn't know any top Tissbury Town coaches, but I did know some grown-ups. Later that morning, while the rest of my class was drawing pictures of dragonflies, I decided to make a list in my notebook (sorry, Miss Patel!):

GROWN-UPS I KNOW

1. Mum
2. Dad
3. Grandpa George (too old to be a grown-up?)
4. Mr Crawley
5. Tabia's mum (NOT a football fan)
6. Mr Mann (NO WAY!!!)
7. Billy's mum (forget it)
8. Miss Patel (travelling to India for the summer)

Hmmm. Once I'd crossed out the last four names on my list, that only left me with four. Well, actually, three (mostly) healthy adults, plus one really old man who knew a lot about football. It wasn't exactly a coaching team that was going to make Paul Porterfield jealous, but with Tabia plus Daniel, it had "potential".

I moved on to Part 2 of my plan: what would each of my coaches DO at the Worldies? With the pressure on, I was going to need a calm, happy camp where everyone knew their roles and worked together for the good of the team. That wasn't going to be easy, though. As you've probably noticed by now, **my family + football = MAJOR FALL-OUTS!**

I couldn't let that happen again. Not with the whole of the Worldies watching. It was time to make a second list:

TIGERS COACHING TEAM

COACH	STRENGTHS
TABS	Mad skillz, best best friend
MR CRAWLEY	very friendly, very proud of his son
GRANDPA GEORGE	Amazing football ideas (like me!)
DANIEL	Scoring loads & loads of goals
MUM	Organizing, running (despite being a grown-up)
DAD	??? Moaning? Boasting about Daniel?

No, no, no, I had to come up with something better than that. What did Dad do best? He could be really funny sometimes, but we already had Tyler, our team joker. He was a good driver, but we wouldn't need cars in Capdevila. He knew lots about computers, but...

Think, Johnny. Think! I bounced ideas around my brain all lunchtime and all afternoon, until, at last, as I kicked a stone home from school ... ***TING! LIGHT-BULB MOMENT!***

Because what did Dad love talking about more than anything in the world, even more than my brother's football future? That's right, his injured ankle!

That evening, when Dad got back from work, I had a very important question to ask him:

"Do you know anything about first aid?"

"Yes, I do indeed!" he replied with real pride in his voice. "I completed the latest course just last week. In fact, I think I've still got the booklet in my bag if you'd like to have a look. What can I help you with? A plaster? Mouth-to-mouth resuscitation?"

"No, thanks. Gotta go. Bye!"

Right, task complete. I was ready to announce the Tigers coaches who were coming to the Worldies with me! But how would I reveal the big news? At a full team meeting? No, that was going to take too long to organize. Just send them all text messages? No, that wasn't my manager style. I wanted to tell them face-to-face, starting with my best friend on the walk to school the next day:

TABS – ASSISTANT MANAGER & SKILLZ COACH

"Nice one, BIN-BREATH. Best friends for ever!" she replied with a smile and our special, secret handshake. "By the way, if you'd asked someone else to be your assistant, I probably wouldn't have spoken to you EVER again."

"Thanks, Tabs. Good to know!"

Mr Crawley was the next name on my coaches list. He lived all the way on the other side of Tissbury, but, luckily for me, he now taught badminton at our school every Tuesday morning. For free! Talk about super friendly, eh?

"Morning, Mr Crawley!" I called out as I entered the sports hall. My words echoed off the walls like Grandpa George telling one of his old stories for the two millionth time. "I've got something I'd like to ask you..."

MR CRAWLEY – GOALKEEPING COACH

"Wow, JB. Thanks. I'd love to come and train Craig at the Worldies!" He was so excited that he spilled a big box of shuttlecocks all over the floor. "I'm really proud of my boy – he's becoming a better keeper every day. But are you sure you want me there?"

"Yes please!" I said straight away. I already had

a feeling that I might need his extra-niceness out in Spain. Because surely no one could fall out with Mr Crawley, not even my football-mad family.

That's what I was hoping, anyway, as I stood up to make my big announcement at Grandpa George's birthday dinner that night.

"Ahem," I fake-coughed to get everyone's attention. "So, as you all know, the Worldies are coming up and I'd like you all to come with me … as coaches."

GULP! Had I just made a terrible mistake? Was this my new worst football idea ever? Oh well, it was too late to take the words back now.

"Oh, Johnny-pops. You spoil me – such a lovely surprise! This calls for a new football diary … and perhaps a new pair of Lycra leggings too…"

"So that's why you wanted to know about my first-aid qualifications! Well, worry not, son. Those Tigers will be very well looked after— Ow, my ankle!"

"Director of Football – what a bobby-dazzling birthday gift! I haven't got a boggle what it means, but count me in."

And Daniel? Well, his cool-kid nods could mean many different things:

a) secretly buzzing
b) seriously not bothered
c) somewhere in between.

But at least it wasn't a big fat "NO!" For now, my Tigers coaching team was complete, and it was time to move on and think about my players.

TIGERS COACHING TEAM

TABS - ASSISTANT MANAGER & SKILLZ COACH
MR CRAWLEY - GOALKEEPING COACH
MUM - TEAM CO-ORDINATOR & FITNESS COACH
DANIEL - SHOOTING COACH
DAD - TEAM PHYSIO
GRANDPA GEORGE - DIRECTOR OF FOOTBALL

CHAPTER 5

WHO WANTS TO COME TO THE WORLDIES? PART II: THE PLAYERS

As the Tigers arrived at training, there was only one thing anyone was talking about – yep, the Worldies! What new boots they were buying for the tournament, which Capdevila superstars they were hoping to see, how much spending money their parents were giving them to take. There wasn't a lot of focus on playing actual football, but I knew the perfect way to burst the "Tigerz on Tour" buzz – get Mum to talk about boring football trip forms.

"Hi, everyone. As you know, I'm Johnny's mummy and – EEEK – the new Tigers Fitness Coach AND Team Co-ordinator! I bet, like me, you can't wait for the Worldies, but I'm afraid that without one of these babies, you won't be going anywhere," she said, pulling a pile of papers out of her strange new "football folder holder" that basically looked like a postbag. "Nuh-uh, my football friends! So please take one and put it somewhere safe. Then when you get home tonight, give it straight to your parents, get them to read and sign, and then bring it back to me at training next week. Gottit, guys?"

"Yes, Mrs Ball," The Tigers mumbled back, as if they were being told off at school.

"Hey, cheer up, and call me Liz. Or 'Lizzie B. Cool' if you like!"

Oh dear. So far, so super embarrassing, but at least the players weren't so "away at the Worldies" any more. It was time to get the Tigers training session started.

After Mum's fifteen-minute warm-up – a really odd mix of running, yoga and ballroom dancing – I split the players up into small groups for some piggy in the middle.

Piggy in the middle, Johnny? you're probably thinking. *A silly playground game?* Well, in the world of proper, grown-up INTERNATIONAL football, it's called a "rondo". Things always sound more stylish in Spanish, don't they? Capdevila were the kings of the rondo, and I'd also seen Tissbury Town practising them during their pre-game warm-ups. Well, if Paul Porterfield thought it was a good idea, then so did I. Anything that might improve our touch and passing under pressure would be super useful for the Worldies.

Like all the best football managers, I walked from group to group with my assistant by my side, watching and whispering:

"Don't worry, Tabs – that's Craig and he's our keeper now."

"I like the look of Reggie – he's got my kind of mad skillz!"

"That's Si, Beardy Jake's mysterious mate – lots of strength, not so much skill. Definitely a defender and NOT a striker."

"Woah, did you see Temba's first touch there? The ball sticks to his boot like glue!"

I could tell that Tabia was really impressed by the Tiger rondos, and so was I. Mostly. There were TWO players, however, whose minds seemed miles away from the session. Dev, our right-winger, was usually Mr Mega-Skilful, but he was more like Mr Mega-Sulky at the moment.

"Is he always that slow?" Tabia asked. "I've seen my great-grandma move quicker than that and she's nearly ninety and both her hips are made of metal!"

I shook my head. "He was super tired at the end of the season but that's because he was also secretly starring in the school play. The final performance was last week, though. He should be back to his best by now."

Just as I said that, Dev tried to play a simple sideways pass but got his legs all tangled up and landed bang on his bum. Yes, something was seriously wrong.

"PLAYER DOWN! ARE YOU INJURED?" Dad yelled out, grabbing his football first-aid kit in a flash. "IS IT YOUR ANKLE?"

"Nah, all good, Mr Ball. I just slipped, innit," Dev muttered back miserably.

I had to find out what was up, and fast. So, as I helped him back to his feet, I gave him a look I like to call, "What's up? You can trust me, I'm your manager!" Dev took a long breath and then let out eight short, worrying words:

"J, can we chat deep for a sec?"

Dev tried to keep things calm, but as soon as we reached the changing room, he slumped down on the bench, head in hands, elbows on thighs, eyes on floor. Oh boy, I knew he was into drama, but this looked bad...

"Soz, J, I've got some proper nasty newz to tell ya. Ya know that school play I was in, yeah? Well, we're going on tour, innit – just like the Tigerz. I already said I'd go but it's the same week as the Worldies. I dunno what to do!"

"Well, which would you rather do?" I asked.

I thought Dev would need time to think about that, but, actually, he already had his answer ready: "Don't get me wrong, I love football and I'm Tigerz for eva, man, but this acting stuff is ACE! Mr Francis says I could go far if I really focus. Only I can't do both. One's gotta go, innit."

I think Dev thought I'd get angry after that and

tell him he was letting the Tigers down, but no way would I ever do something like that. "Look, don't worry about the Worldies," I told him. "Just do what YOU want to do and chase your dreams."

Dev looked relieved, as if he'd just escaped a lifetime detention. "Thanks, li'l man. You're the best boss around!"

As we walked back out onto the pitch together, I did some quick maths in my head:

11 minus Daniel = 10

plus Si = 11

minus Dev = 10

Ten! Uh-oh. We were going to need new players! Six of them if we wanted a full squad for the Worldies, but a minimum of three because there was no way we could succeed without at least a couple of subs. Where on earth were we going to find that many free and talented Tigers in time for the tournament?

Sadly, the situation was about to get even worse. Remember earlier, when I said, "There were TWO players, however, whose minds seemed miles away from the session"? Well, one was Dev, and the other was Tyler. Our team joker had gone too far this time and turned himself into the team tormentor!

While the other Tigers were taking the rondo seriously, he was running around trying to pull players' shorts down! And when Coach Crawley asked him nicely to stop, Tyler grabbed a water bottle and squirted him in the face.

"Soz, didn't mean to cause a splash!" he giggled.

I didn't mind Tyler playing a prank or two at training, but this was way more than that. He was being really rude and ruining the session for everyone else. As Tigers manager, it was my job to tell him off, but what was a nine-and-a-quarter-year-old like me supposed to do with a teenager like him? Make him sit in the naughty corner of the changing room?

If only Daniel had come to training like I'd asked him to, instead of being lazy and staying in bed. He could have talked to Tyler, teenager to teenager, and got him to stop all this silliness.

Never mind, when in doubt, call a ...

"TIME-OUT!"

That gave me a few extra minutes to plan my next move. But after a quick talk with Tabia, I turned around and ... Tyler was nowhere to be seen! Oh no, where was he now and what was he up to?

Stealing clothes from the changing room?

Supergluing the toilet seats?

Setting fire to the corner flags?

No, eventually, I found Tyler in my manager's office/team store cupboard, pouring itching powder all over the spare kits. Enough was enough, so I asked all three of my top questions in a row:

"Ty, what is going on? Why are you behaving so badly? Don't you want to go to the Worldies?"

"Course I do, J, but I can't, can I?" Tyler moaned, crossing his arms like a toddler having a tantrum and kicking over a pile of cones. "'Coz Mum says I'm GROUNDED!"

It turned out that one of Tyler's playground pranks

had gone wrong. Really, really wrong. ("How was I supposed to know that feeding extra-hot chilli con carne to a pigeon would make it explode?") And when she found out that her son had been suspended from school, Tyler's mum picked the worst possible punishment she could think of:

"You can forget about playing football in Spain this summer!"

I'd met Mrs Jenkins enough times to know I had no chance of changing her mind. She could scare off a hungry shark if she had to.

Terrific! Si could take Tyler's place in central defence, but that still left us another Tiger short for the Worldies. It was less than two weeks till the start of the tournament, and I needed to find at least FOUR new players. There was only one thing for it: a team trial.

CHAPTER 6

THE TIGERS TEAM TRIAL

1) A tricky right-winger to replace Dev
2) A star striker to be the "new Daniel" (no pressure!)
3) & 4) ~~Subs~~ "Team players"

Finding at least four new footballers – how hard could it be? After all, we were offering the chance to travel to Spain, have some football fun in the sun and maybe even win the Worldies. What kid in Tissbury could say no to all that?

But first, they needed to know when and where the Tigers Team trial was happening – Saturday morning, 10 a.m., Tissbury Rec, in case you're interested. So, what could we do to spread the word far and wide? WORK TOGETHER, of course!

Dad used his computer skills to post the event all over social media,

Mum used her communication skills to call every

parent in her phone book, and ~~Mr~~ Coach Crawley asked Craig nicely if he could design an "eye-catching" poster for the trial. My expectations were lower than a walrus in a well, but, actually, it looked amazing! Yes, our keeper was 110% better with his hands than his feet.

Perfect! Next, Tabia and I hopped on our bikes and put the posters up all over town, with some help from a temporarily un-grounded Tyler (I managed to persuade his mum that it was "community service"). Now, we just had to sit back and wait for all the incredibly talented kids to show up on Saturday.

At 9.47, our first new footballer arrived, looking super keen in a full Tiger-orange kit. It seemed like a positive sign.

"Hi, Timmy. Good to see you again!" Coach Crawley called out with a friendly wave.

"You know him?" I asked.

"Yes, that's Timmy Chu. He turns up at Tigers pre-season training every year."

"Any good?"

"Well, like everyone in the world, JB, he certainly has his strengths..."

Hmmm. That sounded like a really nice way of saying "no" to me. I looked over at Beardy Jake, who was shaking his head extra hard as if he had a bee in his ear. Yes, definitely a "no".

Right, who else was there? By the time Mum was ready to "get the warm-up party started", we had seven trialists in total:

1) Timmy "I'll do anything!" Chu,
2) a funny and flexible player called Max (or "a foot-ALLer" as he described himself),
3) a "somewhere in midfield"-er called Hamza,
4) a "wicked winger" (his words, not mine)

called Brandon with bright orange boots,

5) a suspiciously old-looking attacker called Ambrose,

6) a scowling striker called Ste ("No, NOT Steve!" I made that mistake and it really didn't go down well)

and

7) a very smiley striker called Rafa.

Seven – it wasn't quite the hundreds I'd been hoping for, but it was still a good, solid number, with room for me to pick and choose the best players. Or, if somehow everyone turned out to be totally amazing, then there was space in our Worldies squad for all of them!

After a warm welcome and a quick who's who of the Tigers, it was time.

"Good luck, everyone – let the trial begin!"

We didn't just go straight to a big game, though. No, no, this was the Worldies we were competing in, so I had asked the Tigers coaches to plan out a whole series of proper football tasks to test the trialists. Meanwhile, I walked around the pitch, watching and working out my manager ratings:

"RUN TILL YA DONE" WITH MUM

TIMMY	A* (for effort)
MAX	A* (for making jokes even on the move)
HAMZA	B+
BRANDON	B- (got off to a bad start by asking, "why would I need to run with mad skillz like mine?")
AMBROSE	D (came last and had to lie down for ten minutes afterwards)
STE	C (came second but tried to trip Timmy up)
RAFA	A

RING-A-RING-A-RONDOS WITH COACH CRAWLEY

TIMMY	B- (tried hard, plus one of the happiest piggies in the middle I've ever seen)
MAX	B
HAMZA	A
BRANDON	B- (shouted "Passing is PANTS!" every time he messed up, which was pretty often)
AMBROSE	A
STE	D (for bad behaviour - booted a ball at Brandon's bum)
RAFA	A*

SKILLZ DRILLZ WITH TABIA

TIMMY	B- (not a wing wizard, but did help collect the cones afterwards)
MAX	B
HAMZA	A
BRANDON	C (a bad footballer blames his bright orange boots)
AMBROSE	A- (very slow, though, like a tortoise on a race track)

STE	F (told Tabs she could "shove yer skillz where the sun don't shine")
RAFA	A

HOT SHOTS WITH ~~DANIEL~~ ME

TIMMY	B- (gave it a go, but not a striker)
MAX	B (nope, not a striker)
HAMZA	B+ (probs not a striker)
BRANDON	B- (too much of a show-off to be a striker)
AMBROSE	B+ (could be a striker, but is he really under 15???)
STE	C (waaay too stressed out to be a striker)
RAFA	A* (at last, looks like a striker!!!)

I had made up my mind about Rafa before we even got to the match at the end – he would be an AWESOME addition to the Tigers Worldies squad. Talent? TICK! Teamwork? TICK! Used to playing in hot temperatures? TICK! You see, Rafa and his family had only just moved to Tissbury from a town in Portugal called Tomar, and he was making football friends already.

"From now on, I'm gonna call you Ronaldo!" I even heard Reggie shout during the Skillz Drillz, which, from him, was the ultimate sign of respect.

What about the other three new Tigers we

needed, though? Rafa had been the only stand-out star so far, but I was hoping that playing a proper match might bring out the best in the others. Unfortunately, however, it mostly just brought out the worst.

As soon as the game kicked off, so did Ste. He raced around the pitch like a rhino looking for revenge, pushing and punching anyone who got in his way. Even big, strong Si looked a little scared of him. When he bit Beardy Jake on the ear, that was it. I decided the boy had to go before he did some serious pre-Worldies damage.

~~STE~~

With Ste sent off, Brandon decided it was his time to shine, and, once he got the ball, he refused to give it back. His feet flapped from side to side in a blur of bright orange boot, but seventeen stepovers later, he was still standing in exactly the same spot! Nope, the Tigers definitely didn't need a "ball grog" like that, as Grandpa George would say.

Right, that only left four more trialists to fill three squad spots, and I still wasn't sure about Ambrose. Although he was a fairly good footballer, he looked so ... old. I know Beardy Jake already had a beard, but this guy had white hair growing out of his nose and ears! And every time he moved (slowly), his knees ticked like a clock.

"Can Ambrose really be the right age?" I whispered to Tabia, who nearly laughed her head off.

"If he's fourteen, then I'm not even born yet!"

She was right. Ambrose had to be lying. I thought about asking to see some ID, but, no, that would be super awkward. So instead, I got an oldie detective to help me.

"You know who you remind me of?" Dad said as he gave Ambrose's dodgy knees a minute of magic spray. "Billy 'The Bathtub' Mullins! But you're probably too young to have heard of h—"

"Heard of him?!" Ambrose exclaimed excitedly,

giving the game – and his real age – away. "I was there at the Railway Road Stadium the day he made his Tissbury Town debut!"

Job done.

"I'd say he's somewhere between forty-seven and fifty-two."

"Thanks, Dad!"

~~AMBROSE~~

There were only three trialists left:

TIMMY

MAX

HAMZA

and we needed at least three players for the Tigers squad. Sadly, we had run out of other options. Max and Hamza both looked like pretty talented team players, but Timmy Chu? Yes, he was keen and good at collecting up the cones, but coming off the bench at the Worldies? He was more likely to be a blooper sub than a super sub.

"Should we take Timmy to the Worldies or not?" I decided to ask my coaches at our after-trial meeting.

"I say yes – he's a good kid," said Coach Crawley.

"I say no – he's not a very good footballer,"

said Dad.

"Don't be so mean, Steven!" Mum told him off. "Well, I say yes. Gotta love a trier, right?!"

2–1 to Timmy. It was all up to Tabia now. "Hey, why not?" She shrugged. "A helpful Tiger might come in handy, and it's not like we have anyone better, is it?"

She was right. Timmy Chu would have to do.

WHAT TO WEAR AT THE WORLDIES?

Coaching team? TICK!

Playing team? TICK!

Right, now that the Tigers were ready for the tournament, it was time to think about myself for a minute. What manager essentials was I going to need for the trip, and, most importantly, what was I going to wear at the Worldies?

NOT Grandpa George's extra-long scarf, that was for sure. I would take it with me for good luck, of course, but it wasn't going anywhere near my sweaty neck.

And I wouldn't be able to wear my favourite tracksuit either. No, out in sunny Spain, my Worldies outfit would need to be something super cool in every way.

I spent all week working on my Worldies look, until, eventually, my wishlist was complete.

There was just one problem: my nine-and-a-quarter-year-old's pocket money wasn't going to stretch to buy everything. Not even close. So, there was only one thing for it:

"Mum, can I come to town with you today?"

"Of course, sweetie. You know how much I love our little shopping trips together," she replied, grabbing the car keys straight away. "Sooooo, watcha lookin' for?"

My list was so long that I thought it would be easier to just hand it over. Wrong! Because instead of taking a quick look, Mum pulled out her reading glasses and took a seat at the kitchen table.

"Travel tactics board, pack of pens, extra notebook – oooh, good idea. Extra whistle, football pump – don't worry, we've got plenty of those in the cupboard...

"...A VEST?!" she cried out suddenly as if it was a swear word or something. "Please tell me that's for the beach and not for the touchline, Johnny-jim-jams!"

"No, not a vest, Mum – a tank top," I tried to explain. "It's different – waaay cooler—"

"Absolutely not! That simply won't do, darling – you've got to look your best for your big moment. Everyone at the Worldies will be watching you, so we can't have you dressed like a scruffy little surfer, can we? No, leave it to me, lovely. I'll find you a nice light summer blazer."

"No way. I'll be boiling and all my amazing ideas will evaporate out of my brain!"

"Don't be so dramatic, dear! A crisp white shirt then, and a tie with tigers on it."

"Mum, I'm nine – not forty-nine!"

"OK, I've got it. How about a smart polo shirt?"

"Fine!" I said. It was definitely the best of the

super-embarrassing bunch, and I knew Mum wasn't going to stop until she'd won. "So, can we go now please?"

Nope, not yet. She hadn't finished reading my list.

"FLIP-FLOPS!"

"They're for the beach, Mum," I lied.

"I should hope so, but you'll be needing some smart shoes to wear on the touchline too."

🏆🏆🏆

"Mum, where are we going?" I moaned, struggling to keep up with her as she marched straight down Tissbury High Street. The new Tigers fitness coach sure could walk fast! We had ages to buy what we needed, but that didn't matter; she was a mum on a smart clothes-shopping mission. "I know the perfect place," was all she would say.

"The perfect place" turned out to be "Priscilla's", a super-posh shop for smartly dressed grown-ups who wanted their kids to look like smaller versions of themselves. Mum had fooled me big time; there wasn't a single polo shirt in sight! Instead, there were bow ties, blazers and turtleneck sweaters everywhere, in every boring shade of green and grey.

When I asked, "Excuse me, have you got anything in orange?" Priscilla just shook her head and sniffed the air as if I'd brought a bad smell into her shop.

"This place sucks. Can we please go somewhere else?" I whispered, but Mum was too busy building the most horrible outfits ever. Honestly, each one was worse than the one before.

Woah! There was no way I was trying ANY of them on! What if someone from school walked past and saw me? Billy the Bully would call me "Johnny BALLGOWN" for the rest of my life. I had to get Mum out of there quickly, but how? *Think, Johnny. Think!*

TING! LIGHT-BULB MOMENT!

"Mum, did you see that?" I shouted, pointing out of the shop window. "Paul Porterfield just walked past!"

I made her look, but not for very long. "Johnny-sweety, are you trying to trick me into leaving this shop because you don't like it?"

Oh man! Mum knew me too well, and that made things a whole lot harder. Oh well, time to add Layer 2 to the Lie Pie.

"No, seriously, I'm sure it was him! And he was walking with a woman I've never seen before – definitely not MRS Porterfield..."

There was no way Mum wouldn't fall for that. Famous football people AND Tissbury gossip – her two favourite things.

"I'm ever so sorry, Priscilla. We'll be back in a bit!" she called out, dragging me along by the arm. "Right, which way did they go?"

Ten minutes of twists and wrong turns later, we "accidentally" arrived back on the High Street, outside "Bats and Balls and Bits and Bobs", Tissbury's number one sports shop.

"Sorry, Mum. We must have missed them somehow," I said, trying my best to sound sad. "Oh well, seeing as we're here, shall we go in?"

"What a shame! But yes, I suppose so, sweetie..."

Bingo. I know, I'm a genius, aren't I? Anyway, Mum was soon so excited by all the sports stuff that she totally forgot about Paul Porterfield, the mystery woman and, most importantly, the posh shop we'd been in before. Poor Priscilla – NOOOOOT!

Item by item, we worked our way through my Worldies wishlist:

Travel tactics board? TICK!

Vest to be worn <u>ONLY</u> at the beach? TICK!

Orange polo shirt? TICK!

"Ooooooh, I could even sew on a little tiger badge to make it look official!"

Finally, Mum and I were on the same football wavelength. "Yes please!" I replied eagerly.

Flip-flops to be worn <u>ONLY</u> at the beach? TICK!

Trainers that looked almost like smart shoes? TICK!

An hour later, we left Bats and Balls and Bits and Bobs with four bags full and Mum's bank account empty. It had turned out to be a successful shopping trip ... in the end. I was now all set. Once my suitcase was packed, it would be "Worldies, here we come!"

HUNGRY TIGER ON THE LOOSE!

"...10 ... 11 ... 12 ... 13 – all Tigers present and correct!"

From the moment the bus arrived to take us to the airport, Mum took her role as Team Co-ordinator super seriously. I mean clipboard-and-spreadsheets super seriously.

"Course we're all still here, Lizzie B. Cool," Reggie reminded her. "Where would we go? We're stuck in a moving vehicle!"

"Yes, I know that, thank you, Reginald, but it never hurts to be organized."

And Mum got even more "organized" once we got to the airport. Every corner we turned or queue we joined meant another new Tiger count.

"Please stop talking, poppets, or

I'll have to start from zero again. Actually, could you all please hold hands and walk in pairs? That would make things much easier—"

"NOOOOOOO!"

Even quiet Connor was moaning after a while. "This is worse than that time we went on a school trip to Tissbury Prison!" I heard him whisper to Noah, who shook his head. "No, this is worse than spending a night *in* Tissbury Prison!"

They were right. Mum wasn't exactly making our journey enjoyable, but who was going to stop her? Not me; not Dad, who was hiding behind his first-aid book; and definitely not Daniel, who had his headphones glued to his ears. My brother had done absolutely ZERO coaching so far, and I had given up asking for his help because he was like a rubbish robot with only one lazy line:

"Soz, I'm on crutches, innit."

Who else – Grandpa George, maybe? She was his daughter, after all...

"Do you think you're maybe molly-coddling us a smidgen, moon pig?" he bravely suggested after Mum had patted down his pockets, pulled out a "suspicious" toffee, and then popped it in her mouth "to do a taste test". But she just gave Grandpa George the "look" and then carried on her pre-security security search.

"Next Tiger please. Arms up..."

Eventually, we reached the fun part of the airport – the land of duty-free shops and restaurants.

"Or 'Last Chance Saloon' as I like to call it, cowboys!" Mum shouted, firing finger-pistols into the air.

Sounds super embarrassing, right? Well, sadly she was only just getting started...

"If you've forgotten something, now's the time to find out. Soooooo, everyone got your passports?"

Head-shakes all round.

"Don't look so worried, Tigers – that was just a test to see if you were listening! I've got them all right here in my football folder holder. What about your spending money?"

Nods all round, plus lots of hungry looks over at the Happy Burger Bar. It was waaaay past lunchtime but Mum kept going:

"Toothbrushes?"

"Pyjamas?"

"Pants/knickers?"

"Your favourite soft toys?"

"Enough, Mum!" I butted in, taking charge of MY football team again. "Tigers, you've got twenty minutes of free time now. I repeat, twenty minutes. Everyone meet back here, OK?"

"Yes, boss!"

And they were off, racing around the airport like it was the last hour at the Tissbury Towers theme park. WARNING: teenagers on tour and on the loose! But would they all find their way back in time for our flight…?

Surprise, surprise, Timmy was the first to return to Tigers base camp, eager and early, closely followed by Hamza, Rafa and Max, and then Connor, Noah, Craig and Temba.

"Eight – we're over halfway there!" Mum cheered, briefly waking Grandpa George up from his "eighty winks".

"What, what, halfway there? Already? Blimey O'Reilly, I don't even remember getting on the plonking plane! Oh well. Zzzzzzzzzzzzzzzzzzzzzzz..."

Finn and Aroon were the next to arrive, right on the twenty-minute mark, with two of the biggest bags of sweets I've ever seen.

"Ten!" Mum punched the air as if she'd scored. "Time for another taste test, methinks. Oooh, you got any fizzy cola bottles in there?"

That still left three Tigers who were now officially LATE. Hmm. It wasn't the best way to start our big trip, was it? I made a note in my brain book – "Talk to the team about discipline ... and how to tell the time". But just as Tabia started thinking up some seriously mean punishments – "How old do you have to be to get a tattoo on your face?" – Reggie and Beardy Jake arrived together in a rush of "Soz!"

and loud pizza burps.

"It's fine, just don't do it again. But where's Si?" My question was aimed at both of them, but mainly at Beardy Jake.

"What you askin' ME for?" he replied with a grumpy shrug.

"Because he's YOUR mate," Tabs backed me up like a top assistant manager.

"Yeah, but I don't know where he is 24/7, do I? I ain't his dad!"

At the sound of that last word, MY dad came rushing over, first-aid kit at the ready. "Tigers Team Physio, reporting for duty! I've got plasters, bandages, wet wipes, a foil blanket..."

"Hmmm. You got any stickers?"

"No, Jacob. I'm a physio, not a dentist."

"Oh, right. Nah, I'm all good thanks, Mr B..."

We waited a few more minutes, but there was still no sign of Si. Uh-oh. Our flight was about to take off and there was still one Tiger on the loose. Where on earth could he be? In airport jail? On the toilet?

"This is the final call for passengers travelling on Flight 212 to Capdevila..."

"Let's just go without that ***FOX FART!***" Tabia

snarled next to me.

No, we couldn't just leave him behind, but were we really about to miss out on our Worldies trip of a lifetime all because of one lost Tiger? Was my journey to become "Johnny Ball: International Football Genius" about to end before it had even begun?

Come on, Si. Hurry up!!

I looked at the screen – "GATE CLOSING!" – and then over at my Team Co-ordinator – "Arggghhh, help me, Mum!"

"Leave it to me, lovey," she said as she marched off. Less than thirty seconds later, I heard a familiar voice making a stern airport announcement:

"Attention – this is an angry call for Si of the Tissbury Tigers. Si, GET YOUR BUTT TO GATE 13 ***RIGHT NOW****!"*

As Mum's words came screaming out of every speaker, Si appeared, strolling slowly towards us with his headphones on and a Happy Burger in each hand.

"What?" he mumbled between mouthfuls when he saw our furious faces. "I was starvin'. Don't judge me!"

We all sprinted for the gate. "WE'RE COMIIIIIIING!"

Mum called out from the front of the long line of Tigers, leaning hard on her wheelie suitcase to push her forward faster.

Gate 13 was totally empty and very much closed when we got there, but luckily, after a few words from Mum, everything magically opened up again.

"W-what did you s-say?" I panted as we legged it along the last walkway that led to the plane.

"Nothing much, munchkin. I just told them that we had a big football tournament to get to. Oh, and that we would sit in Gate 13 and rehearse our 'TIGERZ ON TOUR' football song all night long if they didn't let us through."

"What?"

But never mind my super-embarrassing mum, my uncomfy seat or my lack of legroom – all that really mattered was, we had made it. Phew! Panic over. Despite the Si delay, we were on our way to Spain for the Worldies!!

"Tigerz! Tigerz! Tigerz!" we chanted as our plane took off into the air, until the grumpy man next to Noah asked us all to be quiet. Beardy Jake's reply?

"Booooooooooooooooooooooooooo!"

Oh boy, it was going to be a very long two-hour flight for everyone else. As soon as the seat-belt sign went off, Mum jumped up: "Time for a Tigers team picture!"

"Yeaaaaaah!" cheered everyone.

Well, everyone except me and Daniel. You see, there was a reason that I hadn't asked Mum to be "Team Photographer". That reason? She was *terrible* at taking photos. Absolutely the worst. She could somehow make even the simplest shot turn out blurry, so what chance did she have on a bumpy aeroplane?

That wasn't going to stop her from trying, though. After five minutes of trying to "get the right angle", she found it. Apparently. By putting her elbow in the grumpy man's face.

"Ready? OK, everyone say 'GRRR'. On three: 1, 2, 3..."

"TIGERZ!"

Photo success or photo fail? I think I'll let you decide for yourselves.

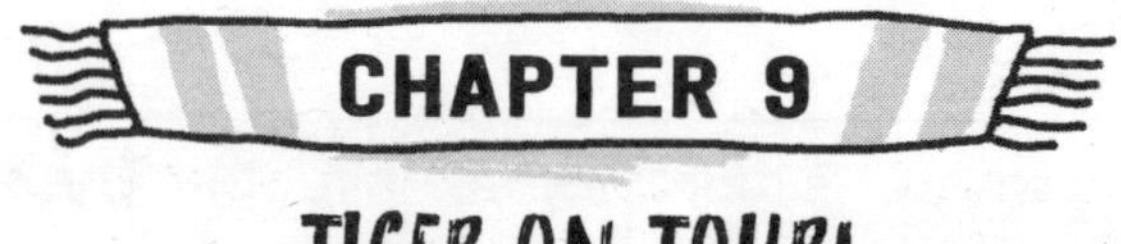

CHAPTER 9

TIGER ON TOUR!

Fortunately for the other passengers on the flight, the Tigers eventually got tired. Surprise, surprise, Si was the first to fall asleep, now that his belly was full of burgers.

"Hey, ***DUCK-DROOL***, are you thinking what I'm thinking?" Tabia whispered, giving me her evilest grin.

Yes, I was – it was the perfect time for Si's seriously mean team punishment, and for the first use of my new pack of manager pens…

"Everyone, meet our new mascot," announced Max, who was quickly taking over from Tyler as the team joker. "We're calling him SIGER!"

HAHAHAHAHAHAHAHA!

Punishment prank complete. Now, it was nap time…

An hour later, our plane landed with a thump and a trumpet blast, shaking everyone awake.

"*Bienvenidos a Capdevila,*" the flight attendant announced.

"You what?" Si mumbled as he rubbed the sleep out of his tiger eyes.

"It means 'Welcome to Capdevila'," Rafa explained. He was from Portugal, not Spain, but apparently a lot of the words are kind of similar. Anyway, with language skills like that, Rafa had just earned himself a new title: Official Team Translator.

"Cool, cheers, Ronaldo. Tigerz on Tour!"

Well, nearly. But first, we had to wait aaaages at passport control. Can you guess why?

"Hmmm," the Spanish guard kept saying, looking up at Si's tiger face and then down at the stripe-less photo in his passport. "You look … different."

"Really? I did have a haircut last week," Si suggested, making scissors with his fingers.

But the guard shook his head. "No, no, not hair – face."

At first, none of us said anything because we were too busy laughing, but the longer it went on, the angrier Si grew.

"Look, stop being mean about my face and just let me through!"

"NO ENTRY!"

"IF YOU DON'T LET ME THROUGH RIGHT NOW, I'M GOING TO WET MYSELF, MATE!"

Uh-oh. Things were starting to get serious now, but, luckily, Rafa came to our rescue.

"*Perdón, señor,*" he said politely to the guard, smudging the stripes on Si's furious face. "*Solo es rotulador.*"

"What? Hey, wait a second. What did you guys do to me while I was asleep?! Someone pass me a mirror..."

Eventually, once Si had calmed down and we'd collected our bags, we all made it out of the airport, hot, hungry and bored, but alive.

"We're here, team!" I called out like a cheesy tour guide. "So how do we get to the hotel, Mum?"

"Actually, you'll have to ask your father about that," she said with a slightly nervous smile. "I decided to leave him in charge of that."

Really?! I tried to stay positive and give Dad a chance.

"Yes, everyone follow me," he said, leading the way with confidence. "The taxis round here will be a rip-off, so let's walk – it's not far!"

Unfortunately, Dad's idea of "far" was a little different from the rest of us. Actually, A LOT different. Twenty minutes of rubbish map-reading later, we were still wheeling our suitcases along the seriously hot streets of Capdevila. With a really steep hill ahead of us, Dad had some difficult questions to deal with:

Dad snapped back. He was losing confidence quicker than a gorilla on a golf course. "Th-think of this as a warm-up, lads. You need to get used to this weather if you're going to play well at the Worldies!"

At last we turned a corner and there it was, the sign we were looking for: "HOTEL HUGO". Well, actually, a few of the letters were missing, so it said "HOT HUG" instead.

"Finally! What took ya so long?" Daniel cried out, banging his crutches against the ground. "Dad, you sure this is the right place? We went in and it looks well whacked out!"

I was pretty sure that wasn't a good thing in cool-kid talk, and Grandpa George confirmed it in old-person speak: "Yes, I have to agree with Daniel on this one. Hugo seems like a very chirpy chappy but his hotel is rather ... higgledy-piggledy."

Yes, as I peered in through the entrance, I could see a leaning tower of dirty plates and water dripping from a pipe into a bucket on the floor.

"Hmmm. No, this can't be the place..." Dad muttered to himself. "I mean, where's the beautiful swimming pool?"

"Oh, there's a pool," Daniel replied, pointing towards the back of the hotel, "but it deffo ain't beautiful. Take a look for yaself."

What used to be a pool was now pretty much a pond. The water had been left for so long that a layer of gross green gunk had grown on top of it and there were all kinds of insects living in it.

"Yuck! Maybe swimming in there should have been Si's punishment," Tabia whispered to me.

I laughed even louder than before because I was trying to block out the embarrassing scene going on in the shady corner behind me:

"Steven, what was I thinking when I asked you to book the hotel?! Did you read the description like I told you to?"

"No, Liz, but it looked so nice in the photos—"

"Did you even check out the reviews?"

"No, but I checked the price, and it was an absolute bargain—"

"Argghhhhh. I gave you one job, Steven. ONE JOB!"

"Liz, can we talk about this later please. Let's not fight in front of the Tigers!"

With that, Mum marched off inside and, with lots of help from Rafa, she managed to have a mostly friendly chat with Hugo. When she returned, she had an update for us:

"Sooooo, Tigers, which would you like to hear first – the good news or the bad news?"

"The bad news please, Mrs Ball," Temba answered politely as Tigers captain. "That way, we end on a positive."

Mum nodded and then took a deep breath: "OK, here goes… Hotel Hugo doesn't have any:

1) air conditioning,
2) swimming pool (well, that it's safe to swim in, anyway…),

3) TV,

4) internet,

5) non-poisonous tap water.

With each problem that Mum mentioned, more and more Tigers sat down in protest, until it was like a game of "last man standing".

"And also only half of the windows open," Rafa added.

That was the last straw for Hamza, which left Timmy as the winner. The rest of the Tigers were having a teenage meltdown. No TV? No internet? Surely that was illegal or something?

Luckily, our captain was still looking for positives. "So, what's the good news then, Mrs Ball?"

"Oh yes. Sorry, Temba. Hotel Hugo does have … AN ALL-YOU-CAN-EAT BREAKFAST BUFFET!"

That got a few half-smiles – who doesn't love free food, right? – but not the loud cheers that Mum was hoping for. Because what if the bread and eggs were as old as the pool water? The last thing we needed was a team of sick Tigers with the Worldies only two days away.

Mum wisely moved straight on to the stuff that she *hadn't* let Dad organize. "OK, shall I tell you who your roomies will be? Everyone will be sharing with one other Tiger, except Grandpa George, because he's not as young as he used to be..."

"Plus, my snores could wake up a woolly mammoth in deepest winter!" he added, almost proudly.

"...and Tabia because ... well, because. So, are the rest of you ready to meet your roomies? Here goes. Connor and Noah..."

Good call! Not only were they brilliant full backs, but they were also best friends, just like:

"...Beardy Jake and Si..."

and

"...Aroon and Finn..."

Our sideways-passing central midfielders were inseparable. Mum had done a super-awesome job of matching everyone up with their mates.

"...Reggie and Temba..."

"...Max and Hamza..."

"...Rafa and Timmy..."

"...Mr Crawley and Craig..."

OK, so *he* didn't look delighted about the idea of sharing with his dad, but Craig didn't complain.

"...and finally, Johnny and Daniel."

That was fine by me. We always shared a room on family holidays, and hopefully this meant my big brother would have no choice but to help me with some of my Worldies ideas. Daniel, however, was definitely "bovvered".

"Nah. Soz, I need my own space. I'm on crutches, innit."

Daniel's answer to everything was no match for Mum, though. "Come on, treacle, there's no 'I' in 'TEAM'!" she said, pinching his cheek in an "I love you but you need to do what I say" sort of way. "We're all in this tournament together, and, besides, I've put you two in the room nearest to the toilets, so you won't have so far to go for your night-time wee-wee."

"Whatevs," Daniel huffed, holding his headphones over his ears to show the conversation was over.

"Great, that's all sorted then. Tigers, follow me!"

As I feared, the bedrooms at Hotel Hugo turned out to be a) boiling hot, b) crying out for a clean, and c) very, very basic. One cupboard, two beds, and one table in between – and a slightly suspicious drainy smell.

"Now, no pillow fights or midnight feasts, OK?" Mum repeated the same not-so-funny line as she showed each Tiger pair to their room.

When, at last, we got to ours, Daniel threw his bag down on the first bed with a lazy, "Crossbar sleeping here," and then hobbled straight out to join the others in Beardy Jake and Si's room, or "The Party Palace" as they were already calling it.

"Yeah, turn this TUUUUUUNE UP!" I heard Reggie yell out over the already-pumping hip-hop music. "Tigerz on Tour!"

As a) the manager and b) a "li'l kid", I knew I wasn't welcome, so I stayed in my room and did some bedtime reading. I hoped the Worldies programme might help to get my football brain busy, but, instead, even the team names were enough to make my head hurt and my tummy go funny:

GROUP A:

Edisonville Elephants (USA)
Blue Bay Barracudas (Australia)
Capdevila Coyotes (Spain)
Longyan Lions (China)

GROUP B:

Saint-Pierre Panthers (France)
Bolgatanga Bears (Ghana)
Rio Alegre Alligators (Brazil)
Tissbury Tigers (England)

GULP! Our opponents all sounded so professional and fierce. What if we lost every single game 10–0 and everyone laughed at us? What if "to do a Tissbury" became a phrase for football teams who turned up but were totally hopeless?

No, we couldn't think like that. We had earned our place amongst the big boys. But now that we had arrived at the Worldies, we really needed to focus on football, and our plan for winning.

"Bedtime, team!" I called out along the corridor. "Get some rest because Tigers training camp starts bright and early tomorrow morning!"

CHAPTER 10

TIGERS TRAINING CAMP

"I know you said bright and early, boss, but this is..."

Before Beardy Jake could finish his sentence – or his second bowl of stale, chewy cereal – his head hit the breakfast table, and he was out: *ZZZZZZZZZZZZ!*

I'll finish his sentence for him: "...6.35 a.m. – a super-sensible time to get started when you're in a seriously sunny place and you only have one day to go before your first really big football match."

Sadly, my team of tired teenagers didn't see it that way. They had been tossing and turning all night, and not because of pre-Worldies nerves; no, because their rooms were hotter than a desert full of dynamite! As I looked around, Timmy was the only Tiger who had both eyes fully open. Hmmm. What a fun training camp this was going to be.

"Look, I'm sorry it's so early and you couldn't

sleep," I said, "but remember: we're NOT on holiday, OK? We've got lots to do and they're saying it's going to be the hottest day of the year. Soon it'll be too hot to even stand up, so come on, let's get going!"

"Yes, WAKEY-WAKEY, my wonderful warriors!" Mum added in her most annoying "I love mornings" voice. "We've got the Worldies to prepare for!"

That got the Tigers moving away from the buffet and, half an hour later, they were all kitted up and ready for football action. Hooray! So far so good, and plus, for the first time ever, I had my full coaching team there with me. Well, Daniel was mostly just sunbathing on the sidelines and Grandpa George was snoozing in the shade, but, hey, it still counts, right?

"Welcome to the Tigers training camp!" I announced. "First up: stretches and sprints with Mu— our Fitness Coach."

GROAN! GROAN! GROAN!

"Come on, there's no need for us to warm up today," Max joked. "We're already roasting!"

That made Mum laugh, but she still made them all do five short sprints each. Even that was enough to send sweat flooding down everyone's faces, and for Dad to run out of emergency ice packs. Tabia and I gave each other a really worried look. This was going to have to be the quickest training camp ever, otherwise the Tigers were going to collapse, one by one.

"Right, one really rapid round of rondos – GO!"

After five minutes, the piggies were melting in the middle.

"Now, line up for a lightning game of pass and shoot!"

Ten minutes later, Timmy was the last Tiger standing again ... and shooting ... wide.

"Unlucky Timmy, top effort! OK, Coach Crawley, can you take Craig for some keeper training now please? The rest of you, let's go through our TOP-SECRET TOURNAMENT TACTICS..."

GROAN!

"...starting with a team talk in the shade."

HOORAY!

Using my travel tactics board, Tabia and I showed the Tigers all of the amazing plans we'd come up with for corners, free kicks and penalties. (Sorry, I can't say any more about them because they're top secret for now, but keep reading and you'll find out!) The players looked excited as they sat there and listened, but less so when we told them it was time to get up and practise.

"Really? Now?" the team all moaned together. "Do we have to?"

"If we want to win the Worldies, YES!"

"Fiiiiiiiiine."

To be fair to the Tigers, they did manage to stay focused for about twenty minutes, but after that, they stopped sticking to the plans and started showing off instead. Fancy flicks, circus tricks, overhead kicks – you name it, they tried it.

"Reggie, can you please promise me you won't EVER do that in a proper game? Right, we're going to end with a match!"

Well, it started off as an actual football match, with the players passing, tackling, running and trying to score goals. But, before long, the sunshine silliness set in.

"These bibs are boiling. My team, let's go skins!" Si declared, taking off his shirt and waving it above his head like a cowboy lasso. Dad raced straight onto the pitch with his emergency sun cream, but Si refused to put any on. "Nah, I'm tryin' to get a holiday tan here, Mr B!"

Meanwhile, Max had gone to get a drink and discovered a bucket full of melting ice, which he was using to "cool his teammates down".

"Heyyyyy! That water went down my shorts, man!" Reggie screamed, chasing after him. "I'm gonna get you back for that..."

Noooo, the Tigers had gone from

total concentration to total CHAOS in sixty seconds! I had to do something before the training camp turned into a full-on battle scene...

Wait a second – ***TING! LIGHT-BULB MOMENT!*** – I'd had an idea. I wanted the Tigers to go into the Worldies feeling good, and what's officially the best way to have fun in the sun? Yes, that's right...

"***TEAM WATER FIGHT!***"

YEAAAAAAAAAHHHHH!

"Thanks for coming, coaches. And sorry about soaking you like that, Grandpa George. I promise I was aiming for Dan–"

"Worry not, whippersnapper. It was absatootly what I needed in this razzling-dazzling weather!"

We were sat around a table in the ~~coolest~~ least-hot part of Hotel Hugo's garden, while the Tigers took naps and dried off after our epic water fight, which had lasted waaaay longer than the football part of the training camp. (Don't worry, no players were hurt in the water-fight fun, other than a few slips and slides).

"Now, as you all know, we've got our first game tomorrow, so I thought we should say a few words about the team, especially the new players and how they're settling in. First up: Timmy."

I only said "a few words" because that's what grown-up people say, but my coaches took it as a challenge.

"Here are three – REAL EAGER BEAVER!" That was Mum who answered, and everyone else agreed.

"Good, that's useful for a sub, I guess... And Max?"

This time, it was Grandpa George's turn: "BORN

BELLY BREAKER. Is that two words or three? I don't have the boggiest..."

A belly breaker – was that a good thing or a bad thing? I wasn't sure, but it sounded painful. Mum must have spotted my "What?!" face, because she translated into modern English.

"Your grandpa means that he's a funny guy and you always need one of those in your group."

"OK. True, but what about on the actual football pitch?"

Coach Crawley decided to give that one a friendly go: "HAS HIS STRENGTHS."

Or, in one word: "sub".

"Right, what about Hamza?"

"DIFFERENT FROM DEV."

"In what way, Dad? Look, you can use as many words as you want, you know..."

"I know, but this is more fun – SOLID OVER SKILFUL."

"OKKKKK... So you think he's more of a hard-working midfielder than a flying winger?"

"YES, THAT'S RIGHT."

"Thanks, and finally, Rafa?"

Tabia took this one for the coaching team: "MAD SKILLZ ... SUPERSTAR!"

I thought we were done, but no, Daniel had to have the last three words, didn't he?

"STRIKER? HATES SHOOTIN'."

A-ha! So, he *had* been watching at the training camp, after all! My first thought was: *No, he's just jealous and he thinks Rafa's going to take his place in the team*. But by thought number six, I was wondering if maybe my brother might be at least a little bit right.

The problem wasn't that Rafa COULDN'T shoot; no, I had seen him score loads of times during our training drills. The problem was that he WOULDN'T shoot, not unless he absolutely had to. You see, unlike Daniel, he wasn't a selfish striker; he was happy for his teammates to grab the glory instead. But as long as the Tigers did well at the Worldies, surely it wouldn't matter who scored our goals?

CHAPTER 11

DUCK, DUCK ... SHOOT!

WORLDIES MATCH 1

TISSBURY TIGERS VS SAINT-PIERRE PANTHERS

"So, who d'ya reckon would win in a fight – a tiger or a panther?"

It was the morning of our first match at the Worldies and we were about to take on the top young team in France, but somehow that was the big issue on Si's mind at breakfast.

I was hoping that, as captain, Temba might tell him to focus on football, but instead he showed off his nature knowledge: "Definitely a tiger. The panther wins on speed, but the tiger would destroy it on size, strength and weight."

"Sweet, so we're gonna win!"

If only it was that simple, but sadly, we weren't actual tigers, and the Saint-Pierre Panthers weren't actual panthers either. We were just two sets of human teenagers – the same age and roughly the same size, speed and strength – and we were battling it out to win the Worldies.

THE WORLDIES – ARGGHHHHH! With less than two hours until kick-off, the alarm bells were really ringing in my brain now. What was I, Johnny Ball, a nine-and-a-quarter-year-old boy from Tissbury, doing managing a team at such a major tournament? What if it turned out to be a total disaster? What if *I* turned out to be a total disaster? As you can tell, I was starting to feel seriously scared and stressed out, and I wasn't even playing in the game. So, surely the Tigers must have been shaking with terror at this point? No, not exactly.

"OK. Well, what about this one, then: a fight between a tiger and a LION?" Si wondered out loud, but, thankfully, before Temba could answer, Mum stood up and made an announcement:

"Righto, tinkers. Time to brush your teeth and grab your kit bags – we're leaving in twenty. Last one at the door's going for a dip in the pool!"

Luckily for Grandpa George, she was joking about that last part, but by 8.28, all thirteen players and seven coaches were waiting downstairs with (mostly) minty breath.

"Phones off, caps on. Let's do this, lovelies!"

The day was heating up faster than a frying pan, but it wasn't far from Hotel Hugo to La Messia, the Capdevila training ground, especially with Mum reading the map instead of Dad. We turned the last corner, and – woah! – it was like walking through the gates of football heaven! Suddenly, everything looked so big and clean and bright – the green of the grass, the white of the lines, the purple of the Saint-Pierre kits. Aroon said what all of us were thinking:

"Woah, this is the REAL DEAL!"

All of the Worldies matches were taking place at La Messia, except for the grand final, which would be played at Parc Vell, the club's proper 70,000-seater stadium. I hadn't told the Tigers about that yet, because I didn't want them to get carried away. We had a lot of games to win before that, starting with Saint-Pierre.

"This is it, team. Our Worldies adventure starts here!" I told them once they'd finished their matchday warm-ups. "Yes, this is going to be our toughest game yet, but that doesn't mean you have to do anything differently. Just more of the same, boys. If we play the way we did against the Kingfishers, then we've got this!"

Yeaaaaaah!

Then Captain Temba took over for the final team huddle bit: "Right, Tigerz. On three: 1, 2, 3..."

"**TIGERZ!**"

La Messia had full-on football dugouts with big comfy seats, but there was no way I was going to sit down to watch the match. This was football, not a film! Plus, for my amazing ideas to appear, I knew I had to be up close to the action.

So, with my cap on (frontwards for once) and my face covered in sun cream, I stood on the sideline instead, ready to clap and cheer my team on.

Although none of our supporters had been able to come with us to Spain, we did at least have the loudest and most-embarrassing coach in the entire competition.

"Gooooooooooooo, TIGERS! Let's pummel these guys into Panther mash!"

Thanks, Mum ... I think. Oh, and we also had the Worldies' best subs-bench boy band too. With Max on words and Timmy on lead vocals (plus Grandpa George as a slightly croaky backing singer), they put on an excellent pre-game concert, featuring classic hits including:

"Eye of the Tiger",

"Smells Like Tiger Spirit",

"When the Stripes Go Marching In",

"What a Wonderful Worldies",

"Johnny B. Great"...

Seconds before kick-off, however, their singing stopped. It was time for the Tigers to get fully football-focused.

Things to do in the first minute of any match (but especially a really major one):

1) Take your time.
2) Get into the game.
3) Keep things safe and simple.

Things <u>NOT</u> to do in the first minute of any match (but especially a really major one):

1) Take risks.
2) Get caught out.
3) Keep things SLOPPY and SILLY!

You don't need to be a football genius to know all that, but, hey, we all make mistakes, right? Well, the Tigers started making them straight from the kick-off – OUR kick-off!

Temba tapped it to Reggie,

who messed up a rabona flick to Finn,

who scuffed his sideways pass to Aroon,

who sliced the ball back to Si,

who bumped into Beardy Jake,

who bumped into the Saint-Pierre striker – in the box ... PENALTY! –

who sent Craig the wrong way from the spot. 1–0!

Oh boy, what a way to start the Worldies! Talk about first-minute madness, eh? While the Tigers were still sleeping, the Panthers had pounced. And things nearly got worse when Si blasted the ball back to Craig at head height, but luckily because of the seriously hot weather in Capdevila, it was soon time for a ...

"**DRINKS BREAK!**"

Perfect. While Timmy handed out the water

bottles and Max squirted the Tigers in the face with his new water pistol, I gave a super-fast team talk that went like this:

"WAKE UP AND STOP BEING SO SLOPPY AND SILLY!"

It took a few more minutes and a few more mistakes, but, eventually, the Tigers did come alive. They passed (properly) and moved, and began to play like a (proper) team again. But while we were definitely getting better and creating more chances, at half-time, it was still 1–0 to the Panthers.

"Keep going. The goal is coming!" I urged the Tigers on. "Finn and Aroon, get the ball FORWARD, and faster. And Rafa, don't be afraid to go for goal yourself sometimes!"

Sadly, Daniel's three words had been spot-on so far – "STRIKER? HATES SHOOTIN'." Rafa was doing everything else right, but it was like he was scared of scoring or something. Why couldn't he just curl the ball into the top corner like he did in training? When Temba put him through one-on-one with the keeper, he had passed to Reggie instead. And when Hamza's cross landed right on his head in the box, he had flicked the ball Temba-wards, not goalwards.

Oh, and speaking of Hamza, I know I don't often

say this, but Dad was right: he was different from Dev. Other than that one cross to Rafa, he had been almost invisible in attack, which got me thinking...

TING! LIGHT-BULB MOMENT!

You see, to go on and win the game, the Tigers would need to equalize early in the second half, so it was time for me to be brave with my team formation. 4-4-2 just wouldn't do! This wasn't the match for wing backs on the counter-attack, but maybe it was the match to try ... a frightening front three!

Yes, 4-3-3 would set our forwards free!

Rafa, Temba and Reggie all attacking together, with Finn, Aroon and Hamza behind them, winning the ball in midfield.

"You're a genius, ***BEETLE-BRAIN!***" Tabia said when I told her my idea, and Reggie loved it too.

"So, basically, I'm all about attack and I don't have to defend any more? Sweeeeeet. Mad plan, li'l man!"

But was it going to work and get the Tigers back into the game? The Panthers were no pushovers; they were strong in defence and their central midfielders were super stylish. They looked like they could keep the ball all game long without even sweating, let alone actually giving it away.

However, there were only two of them and now there were three of us – Finn, Aroon AND Hamza...

YOINK – STEAL! Suddenly, our midfield warriors were winning the battle and then passing the ball forward – hooray! – to the front three. First, Temba burst into the box and forced the Panther keeper to make a super save, then Rafa panicked and sent a weak shot trickling wide.

"Unlucky, keep shooting!"

The Tigers were playing really well now, but – arggghhhh – time was running out! We had to score soon otherwise we were heading for a first Worldies defeat. *Think, Johnny. Think!* I decided to send on our subs for the final five minutes to a) keep the whole squad happy and b) add some extra energy in midfield.

"Good luck, guys – and if you get the ball, give it straight to one of the forwards," I told them both, but especially Timmy.

"Yes, boss!"

Well, guess what! Timmy did exactly what I asked him to. He got the ball and he gave it straight to Reggie, who skilled his way past one defender and then another, until eventually he was fouled just outside the penalty area.

Free kick! OK, this is where you get to find out about those TOP-SECRET TOURNAMENT TACTICS we worked on at the Tigers training camp. Well, one of them, anyway...

Reggie got up and grabbed the ball. "I've got this," he told the other Tigers loudly and then looked over at me and made a "D" with his fingers.

Good choice, Reggie! I gave him two thumbs up, and then he covered his mouth with his hand like the pros do to pass the message on to the others. I can tell you what he said, though:

"DDS."

With two nods, Beardy Jake and Simon walked off and positioned themselves at either end of the Panthers wall.

DDS?! you're probably wondering, while trying to crack the code. Well, let me explain – it stands for:

Duck...

When the referee blew the whistle, Beardy Jake suddenly fell to the floor like he'd been shot by a sniper. That sent the Panther keeper flying to his right post, thinking that was where Reggie's free kick was going.

...**D**uck...

But a few seconds later, Si did the same thing on the other side of the wall, sending the keeper all the way back across his goal to his left post.

...**S**HOOT!

In the end, Reggie curled the ball into the top corner of the poor confused keeper's goal.

GOOOOOOOOOAAAAAAAAAAAALLLLLLL!!!!!

Worldies, Schworldies! There was no way I was going to keep calm when my team had just scored the greatest free-kick goal ever.

"We did it! We did it!" I shouted, as Tabia and I raced onto the pitch (sorry, ref!) to join in the team celebrations.

And also win, schwin. In that mega moment, it didn't matter that we hadn't won our first match. The main thing was that we hadn't lost. A draw gave us one point. We Tigers were officially off the mark at the Worldies!

WORLDIES MATCH REPORT 1 JNB

TISSBURY TIGERS 1–1 SAINT-PIERRE PANTHERS

STARTING LINE-UP (MARKS OUT OF 10):
Craig 6, Noah 7, Connor 7, Jake 7, Si 7, Finn 6, Aroon 6, Hamza 7, Rafa 6, Temba 7, Reggie 8

SUBS:
Max 6, Timmy 8

SCORER:
Reggie

WHAT WENT WELL:
1. We didn't lose.
2. We scored a (great) goal (eventually!).
3. We showed our strong Tiger spirit to fight back after that first mad minute.

EVEN BETTER IF:
1. We had won.
2. We had been more attacking.
3. We had scored more goals.

CHAPTER 12

MISSION GET MORE GOALS

That evening, while the Tigers turned up the "tuuuuuuunez" in Beardy Jake and Si's "Party Palace", I went to visit Grandpa George to get his thoughts on our draw against the Panthers.

"C-COME IN!" he called out in his best "No, old people aren't always napping" voice, but he didn't fool me.

"Apologies for the PJs, my penny-farthing," Grandpa George sounded a bit groggy as he sat down on his bed and patted the space next to him for me. Our chats were always better in chairs and with cups of tea, but this would have to do at Hotel Hugo. "I was just about to take a little late-afternoon snoooooooze, you see. What is it they say, 'When in Spain, do as the Spainish do'?"

No, that's not what anyone says – except Grandpa George – but it wasn't worth correcting him.

Oh, I should tell you about his terrific pyjamas, though. Despite the seriously hot weather, he was wearing a very smart purple long-sleeved shirt and trousers set, with little gold pineapples all over them, plus a matching sleeping hat.

"Sorry, Grandpa. I'll let you sleep in a minute, but first, I wanted to talk about today's game."

"Ah, yes. Well, it was a fair old scuffle out there, but we got there in the end, didn't we? Mind you, we'll have to be more nifty in the next match, and there is one thing I'm wobbling about."

"And what's that, Grandpa?"

"Goals, my boy. None of the Tigers seem to know how to put the ballooning ball in the nodding net!"

Grandpa George was right, of course. While it was important to stay solid at the back, we also had to look dangerous in attack, and since my brother's injury, we had only scored two goals in two games. There was no way we were going to win the Worldies like that.

"I know, but Daniel's supposed to be our shooting coach and so far, he's done nothing! And Rafa's a really good player but he's not a striker."

"Yes, that sonny's a little shot-shy, that's for sure-fire. But it takes more than one egg to make an omelette, and if you drop one, you need to have extra back-ups in the box, if you get my meaning."

"No, sorry, Grandpa. I don't."

"Strikers are always supposed to be the super-duper-stars, but they're not the only ones who can grab a guffing goal, are they? Back in 1956, our top scorer was Tommy 'The Basher' Boswell, and he was a centre back. Any player can do it, even the codswalloping keeper!"

"What, even Craig?"

"Hmmm. OK, perhaps not Craig, but my point is, scoring more goals is a task for *all* the Tigers – every single Sunny Jim of them. Football isn't just about the fancy pants up front – it's about the whole tiddly team working together. Once you've got that right, the goals will come guzzling out like brown sauce from the bottle."

Once again, Grandpa George had got my football brain buzzing big time. What would I do without him? Come up with way fewer ideas, that's for sure!

"Thanks, I'd better go, Grandpa – I've got wallops of work to do."

"My plinking pleasure, miladdy. Oh, and could you tell Daniel I'd like to have a little jibber-jabber with him after dinner please? Well, cheerio. Time for me to catch my eighty winks!"

With Grandpa George's weird and wonderful (and really old) words still spinning around my head, I rushed back to my room to write them down in my notebook. As I got there, Daniel was just hobbling out, but I managed to pass on the message.

"Laterz," my brother replied.

"Yeah, don't go now – Grandpa's having a nap."

"Nah. LATERZ," Daniel said, waving at me.

Oh right, cool-kid talk was really confusing.

Anyway, ahhhhh, quiet at last! With my brother gone, it was just me and my buzzing football brain. We only had one more training session to prepare for our next Worldies group game, so I needed to get straight to work on – dun dun duuuuuuun – MISSION GET MORE GOALS!

Grandpa George was right; Rafa wasn't the only reason why the Tigers were struggling to score. The other forwards, Temba and Reggie, had only got one goal each. Hopefully, they'd all be sharper now that they were part of a new front three. (Plus, Daniel might start doing his job...)

And then there was the midfield – Finn, Aroon and Hamza. We were going to need them to be a lot more attacking for the rest of the Worldies: more forward passes and more forward runs. There were three of them, so even if two of them stayed back, that still meant one could be...

TING! LIGHT-BULB MOMENT! BOX-TO-BOX! Yes, that's what the Tigers needed – a box-to-boxer, making smart moves to score great goals! So, which of our midfielders would be the best at it?

Aroon?

Finn?

Or Hamza?

Hmmm. Sorry if this sounds mean, but they weren't the most exciting options I'd ever been offered. They were all so ... safe and sideways. I just had to hope that one of them would surprise us during our next training session.

🏆🏆🏆

"Tigers, everyone feeling good and fairly cool?"

"Yes, boss!"

Instead of early morning, we had switched the training session to early evening, which made me the most popular manager in the whole Worldies. For a few hours, anyway.

"Right, you know the drills – warm-up, then rondos. Go, go, go!"

After that, it was time for the activity that Tabia and I had been planning all morning: "DEFENCE VS THE REST", or what we were secretly calling "Quest for the Best Box-to-Boxer".

The idea was simple: one by one, the midfielders would practise making late runs to join the attack, and whoever got the most goals and assists would become our box-to-boxer. Gottit? But just as we were about to begin, something weird happened:

"What d'ya want me to do then, J?"

Yes, that was Daniel, and he was offering to help me! Was that what Grandpa George's jibber-jabber had been about? Who cared? I answered straight away, just in case he changed his mind:

"Help Rafa become a more selfish striker … pleeeeaaaase!"

"All right, but I'm gonna need Craig too."

"Of course, yeah. He's all yours!"

So off went Daniel, Rafa and Craig to the other end of the pitch to practise … well, actually I don't really know what they practised because I was too busy focusing on "Quest for the Best Box-to-Boxer". And here's how it went:

ROUND 1

1) Aroon – panicked and played it to Reggie instead, who scored past Coach Crawley (nice coach, bad back-up keeper). ***ASSIST!***
2) Finn – Temba's pass was perfect, but somehow he messed up his shot so badly that the ball didn't even move. ***MISS!***
3) Hamza – Reggie rolled the ball across the six-yard box and all it needed was a tiny tap-in, but, instead, he somehow blasted it waaaay over the bar. ***MISS!***

Results of Round 1 – ***RUBBISH!!!***

ROUND 2

4) Aroon – brave enough to shoot this time, but failed to hit the target. ***MISS!***

5) Finn – first player to hit the target (hooray!), but an easy shot to stop, even for Coach Crawley. ***SAVED!***

Oh boy, this was going to be a looooong game! But just as I was about to give up, up stepped…

6) Hamza – this time, Temba pulled the ball back to him just outside the penalty area, and with a beautiful flick of his right boot, he curled an unstoppable shot into the top corner. ***GOAL!***

Wow! Tabia and I turned and gave each other a "Wait, did that really just happen?" look. But it had, and to prove it wasn't a fluke, Hamza hit two more long-range rockets in Rounds 3 and 4. Our quest was over; we had a winner.

"Well done, Hamza. You're our new box-to-boxer!" I declared. "But maybe don't shoot if you're past the penalty spot, OK?"

"Yes, boss!"

"Mission Get More Goals – TICK!"

Hamza seemed really happy as the Tigers walked off the training field, and so did Rafa, although he was always smiling.

"So, how did your shooting session go?" I asked Daniel, but his only response was, "Fine" and a shrug.

I guess we would just have to wait and see how many goals we scored in our second Worldies group game.

FROM HEROES TO ZEROES IN FORTY MINUTES

WORLDIES MATCH 2:

TISSBURY TIGERS VS BOLGATANGA BEARS

"It depends on the bear, really," Temba said, answering Si's latest animal battle at breakfast. "If we're talking polar, panda or spectacled, then the tiger wins for sure, but if it's a grizzly, then that's a proper fair fight. Those guys can weigh as much as 360 kilograms and run as fast as 35 miles per hour!"

"Hmmm. Doesn't say what kind they are," Si replied, reading my Worldies programme. "Just 'Bears'. Oh well, let's hope they're not grizzlies then!"

The Bolgatanga Bears were, in fact, teenage humans (how many times did I have to explain they're just team names, Si?!) who happened to be really talented at football. They were the Champions of Ghana, the best young team in Africa, and their star striker, Adjo Mensah, was so good that Capdevila had just signed him for £20 million!

"No worries. We'll keep 'im quiet, won't we, mate?" Beardy Jake said confidently as we all stood together in our team huddle a few hours later, moments before kick-off.

"Y-yeah," Si agreed eventually, but he didn't sound so sure, or so happy.

As I looked around, Si wasn't the only Tiger who seemed a bit nervous, but that wasn't such a bad thing. If we'd been a little less relaxed against the Panthers, perhaps we could have won that game and we wouldn't have to worry about beating the brilliant Bears now... But no, there was no point thinking like that. What was drawn was drawn; we had to move on and focus on the difficult match ahead of us.

"We're going to stick with the 4-3-3 formation today," I explained. "I know these guys are good, but I want us to attack as well as defend today. Hamza, remember: you're our box-to-boxer now."

OK, now for a final bit of must-win motivation:

"Oh, and before you go out there, I've got some big news, boys – there will be ... WORLDIES BONUSES!"

Dad swung round and gave me his shocked face, like I'd just let a burglar into our house. Oops, I should probably have checked this part of the plan with my parents first, but they were generous people and obviously I couldn't afford to pay out of the pocket money they gave me.

"Any Tiger who scores a goal gets a free ice cream..."

"Sweeeeeet!" shouted Reggie. "I can have a flake with mine too, right? My free kick was banging!"

"...and if we win today, we'll buy a big fan for each and every bedroom!"

"SWEEEEEET!" shouted all thirteen Tigers, and all the coaches too (except Mum and Dad, of course). If we could just beat the Bears, Hotel Hugo would be horribly hot no more.

"Right, Tigerz. On three," Temba called out in the team huddle. "1, 2, 3..."

"TIGERZ!"

Fortunately, there was no first-minute madness this time. No, the Tigers 1) took their time, 2) got into the game, and 3) kept things safe and simple, until – ***BAM*** – fifth-minute magic!

Like most great Tiger moves, it all started with Temba, who controlled Craig's long goal kick as easily as trapping a fly under a frying pan. As he looked up, Reggie and Rafa were both being marked tightly, but then he spotted it – our box-to-boxer on the move...

"Pass it!" Hamza called out and Temba always did what he was told.

As the ball arrived, Hamza was so far from goal that the Bolgatanga defenders didn't even bother closing him down. Biiig mistake! Because, with another beautiful flick of his right boot, he fired an unstoppable shot into the top corner. 1–0 to the Tigers!

GOOOOOOAAAAAAAAAAALLLLLLLL!!!!!!!!!!!

I know I normally hate the things silly football people say, but "WHAT A SCREAMER!" and

"WHAT A STROKE OF TACTICAL GENIUS!" I even did the whole "rub the eyes and blink" thing they do in films because I seriously couldn't believe what I'd just seen. Yes, I had lots of amazing football ideas, but they didn't normally work THAT well or THAT quickly. It's one thing to score a worldie at training, but our new box-to-boxer Hamza had just scored a worldie ... *AT THE WORLDIES!*

"H, you hero!" Reggie yelled as the whole team celebrated together. "You deserve at least five flakes in your ice cream for that!"

Yes, even Dad couldn't argue with that.

"Well done, Tigers – now CONCENTRATE!" I shouted, poking my brain with two fingers like that weird guy Mum told me about who could bend spoons with his mind.

It was great that we were winning, but the Bears were too good to give up that easily. I knew it was only a matter of time before they bounced back, and that time turned out to be twenty-seven minutes forty-three seconds, as Operation Keep Adjo Mensah Quiet came to an early, messy end. First, he fooled Si with a nutmeg flick and then he skilled his way past Beardy Jake with a stepover snapback. Craig did well to quickly stretch out his really long, thin ruler legs, but even they couldn't stop Adjo's accurate shot into the bottom corner. 1–1!

Some players are just so awesome that when they're at their awesomest, there's nothing you can do to stop them. My brother was one of them, and Adjo was another, but Beardy Jake didn't seem to see it that way.

"Why'd ya dive in like that, mate?" he snarled at Si. "That goal's on YOU!"

"What? Why? I didn't see YOU stopping him!" Si snarled straight back. "It's not my fault he made fools of us both!"

If the score had still been 1–1 at the half-time break, I think they would probably have cooled down and their clash would have ended there. But the Bears' second goal arrived just before the whistle. It was Adjo again, weaving his way past one centre back and then the other … again. 2–1!

Uh-oh. We were losing, and as the two teams walked off the field, Beardy Jake was really boiling with rage. As team captain, Temba tried his best to be the peacemaker, but Beardy Jake stomped straight past him and up to Si.

"You're not fit to tie Tyler's laces," he shouted. "I wish he was 'ere instead of you!"

What was going on? They were supposed to be mates! This time, Si didn't try to fight back; he just stormed straight off to the changing rooms. I could tell that Beardy Jake had planned to do the same, but his centre-back partner had stolen his idea, so he stormed off in the opposite direction instead.

"Do you think we should we go after them, JB?" Coach Crawley asked.

"Not yet," I decided, "let them both cool down for a few minutes first. They'll probably come back."

But I was wrong. At the end of my Tiger team talk (short version: "It's not over. We can do this, but we need to SCORE!"), they were both still missing.

"OK, *now* we should go after them," I said.

Coach Crawley and Mum went looking for Si, while Dad and Tabia went after Beardy Jake, but both search parties came back without centre backs.

"Unfortunately, Si found the club canteen. He's two burgers down already, and he's just ordered another. I think we'll have to sub him off, JB. Otherwise he'll be sick on the pitch."

"Sorry, we tried but we couldn't get Beardy Jake

off the exercise bike at the gym. I've never seen anyone pedal that angrily."

Noooooo! What a Worldies nightmare!

"OK, Max, Timmy – get warmed up. You're going to be our centre backs for the second half."

"Yes, boss!"

Although they weren't as big and strong as Beardy Jake and Si, Max and Timmy made up for that with their energy, enthusiasm and burger-less bellies. They rushed around the pitch like terriers in a toyshop, and together they managed to keep Adjo Mensah quiet ... mostly.

Meanwhile, at the other end of the pitch, the Tigers pushed forward on the attack. Rafa and Temba were running the show with their touch and skill, and even Aroon and Finn were

tiptoeing their way towards the Bolgatanga box! Pass and move, pass and move – our build-up play was better than ever, but when it came to shooting, sadly it was the same old, unsuccessful story:

Temba's cheeky chip bounced off the top of the crossbar and over. SO CLOSE!

Reggie played a silky one-two with Rafa, but then smashed his shot straight at the keeper. SAVED!

It was like the Bears had put a curse on any player who entered their penalty area. How many chances did we need to put the ballooning ball in the nodding net?!

The answer was "a lot", but with five minutes to go, it seemed like we were finally about to equalize. After a Tiger-record eighteen passes in a row, Temba set Rafa through on goal. He was past the last defender, with just the Bears keeper left to beat...

"Go on! You can do it!" we coaches screamed together. But instead of racing forward with fire in his eyes, Rafa kept looking back over his shoulder for support.

"NO, *YOU'VE* GOT THIS!"

As he entered the penalty area, the keeper even slipped, leaving Rafa with an almost-open goal.

He had to score ... didn't he?

No, his shot was so shaky and weak that a defender had time to get back and clear it off the goal line.

MEGA MISS!

"Heavens to Betsy!" Grandpa George cried out. "How did he foozle that?"

Good question! It was my second "rub the eyes and blink" moment of the match – had Rafa really managed to mess that up? Even I could have scored it! I looked over at Daniel, our SHOOTING coach, but he just shrugged back with a little smirk that said,

"Not my fault, bro. It ain't easy findin' a super-striker like me!"

After that, it was game over. The Tigers had lost all hope of beating the Bears, and Adjo Mensah swooped in to complete his hat-trick. 3–1!

The Tigers were about to lose for the first time in twelve matches and I was about to lose for the first time ever as a football manager. Double-disaster!

I felt like I'd really let my team down because, for once, my amazing football ideas had failed me.

Wing backs on the counter-attack? No good.

Fancy free kicks? No good.

Clever corner kicks? No good.

As I stood there on the sidelines, my heart sank so low that it made my tummy hurt. I guess now I knew the real meaning of the word "gutted".

A 3–1 defeat was so disappointing, but that scoreline didn't tell the full story, because we had been by faaaar the better team in the first five minutes and for most of the second half too. I tried telling the Tigers that after the game, but they were too bummed out to believe me.

Two matches, one point and ZERO wins – there wasn't a lot for us to feel positive about, least of all the league table:

Position	Team	Played	Won	Drawn	Lost	Total
1	Bolgatanga Bears	2	2	0	0	6
2	Saint-Pierre Panthers	2	0	2	0	2
3	Rio Alegre Alligators	2	0	1	1	1
4	Tissbury Tigers	2	0	1	1	1

Oh boy, we were now bottom of the group! Was this the end of our Worldies adventure already? Or could we magic up a miracle in our final game?

WORLDIES MATCH REPORT 2 JNB

TISSBURY TIGERS 1–3 BOLGATANGA BEARS

STARTING LINE-UP (MARKS OUT OF 10):
Craig 6, Noah 6, Connor 6, Jake 2, Si 2, Finn 5, Aroon 5, Hamza 7, Rafa 9, Temba 6, Reggie 6

SUBS:
Max 6, Timmy 6

SCORER:
Hamza

WHAT WENT WELL:

1. we scored, thanks to our new box-to-boxer.
2. Our attacking build-up in the second half was awesome!

EVEN BETTER IF:

1. we had won.
2. Our centre backs hadn't been at war with each other .
3. Rafa had been less scared of shooting.

HELP! EMERGENCY COACHES' MEETING

No one said a word on the slow, sad walk back to Hotel Hugo, so I used the time to make a new to-fix list in my head:

TOP 5 TIGER PROBLEMS TO SOLVE:

1. MAKE SURE BEARDY JAKE & SI ARE MATES AGAIN.
2. HELP RAFA TO BE LESS SCARED OF SCORING (& MORE LIKE DANIEL!).
3. GET ALL THE TIGERS SCORING MORE GOALS.
4. LIFT THE TEAM SPIRIT (V. LOW RIGHT NOW).
5. WORK OUT HOW TO WIN AGAINST THE ALLIGATORS (SUPER-AMAZING FOOTBALL IDEAS NEEDED!).

That was definitely too many things for one young manager to try to fix on his own, especially when our next match was only one day away. Why did everything have to happen so fast in tournament football? That was definitely my least favourite thing about it. Back home, I had a whole week to come up with my next amazing football ideas, whereas here, I had less than twenty-four hours to save the Tigers from a Worldies catastrophe. The pressure wasn't just on me; it was all over me, making me feel hot and itchy, like a gnome with a nappy rash. Arggggghhhhh! There was nowhere near enough time for me to think everything through, so I had no choice but to ask for ... HELP!

"Welcome to this emergency coaches' meeting," I said, passing cold cans of iced tea around the table. I placed my travel tactics board in the middle, with my list of "Top 5 Tiger Problems to Solve" written on it for everyone to read. "Thanks for coming, and sorry, Grandpa George – there'll still be time for a nap before dinner, I promise. OK, let's get straight to Problem Number 1 – the argument between Beardy Jake and Si. Daniel, you know them best – what's going on?"

My brother shrugged. "Just a bit of beef, innit. It'll all be sorted by breakfast tomorrow."

"Really?" I replied. "It must have been more than that – they both missed the second half!"

"No, I'm with Daniel on this one," Dad said, like always. "Those boys were just being bad losers – that's all. Let them sort it out amongst themselves, I say."

"For the first time in a long time, I actually agree with you, Steven," Mum admitted. "Well, mostly. However, those lovelies really let the team down today and they shouldn't get away with that. Johnny-kins, you're the manager of course, but if it was up to me, I'd give them a strong telling-off."

Or another of Tabia's seriously mean team punishments? No, I needed them uninjured...

"OK, leave that one to me," I said. "I'll investigate. On to Problem Number 2 – Rafa and his shooting."

This time, Daniel spoke without even being asked to. He wasn't going to miss his chance to say, "I told you, bro! I tried, but he just ain't a striker and he never will be. You gotta be nasty and selfish, not nice and smiley."

"Yes, I know, but could you at least try one more time at training tomorrow? Come on, you're meant to be one of our coaches!"

"What's the point? He ain't got that GOAL-den touch, bro!"

"Pleeeeaaaase?"

"Whateva. Just wake me up for dinner, yeah?"

Problem Number 3 – other Tigers scoring goals – I gave to Tabia. Hopefully she could pass on some of her own awesome attacking skills.

"I know we lost, but our build-up play was really good against the Bears. If we can just add goals to our game, we could still win! Or our next match, at least..."

"Gottit, Johnny – I'll do my best to turn those ***SCAREDY SLUGS*** into ***GOAL-SCORING GODS!***"

Problem Number 4 – team spirit – I gave to Mum.

"Oh goodie, I know just the thing to give those Tiger tots a great big boost – ZUMBA!"

"Really, Mum? I don't think they're in the mood for dancing right now..."

"Nonsense, one of MY Zumba classes can cheer up any sad little sausages!"

I wasn't sure about that, but I was too tired to argue any more. Finally, Problem Number 5 – any intel on the Alligators – I gave to Coach Crawley.

"They're staying down the road at Casa Clara. They have a bar there and it's showing the Capdevila match tonight on TV. Be friendly and find out as much as you can."

"Isn't that ... cheating?"

"No, Coach, it's ... scouting. Cheating would be putting poison in their drinks. DON'T do that!"

"OK, you're the boss, JB!"

"And what about me?" Dad asked.

Good question! Yes, what about Dad? All this quick-thinking was starting to hurt my head... ***TING! LIGHT-BULB MOMENT!***

"I want you to do Tiger fitness tests tomorrow. See if anyone has an injury that we don't know about yet."

"Will do, son. I'll have my magic spray refilled and at the ready!"

"And what about me, miladdy?" Grandpa George asked.

"Our emergency meeting is over – it's time for you to take your nap."

"Oh, that's spiffing. Cheerio, everyone!"

THE "ONLY MATES CAN ESCAPE" ROOM

After a delicious dinner and a decent night's sleep (even though we lost, Mum made Dad buy fans for all the bedrooms anyway – hooray!), I woke up the next morning feeling refreshed and ready to fix things, starting with Beardy Jake and Si's friendship. However, by the time the rest of the Tigers had finished their breakfasts, our sulking centre backs were still nowhere to be seen.

"Maybe they've gone out for an early morning run together," I said super hopefully, "but I'll just go upstairs and check."

When I got there, the signs didn't look good. The piece of paper saying "PARTY PALACE" was still stuck to their bedroom door, but an extra bit had been added underneath and underlined:

"CLOSED 4 EVA!"

Uh-oh.

I knocked nicely a few times – no answer.

I called out to them in a calm, friendly voice – still no answer.

It was only when I banged extra hard with my fist that Beardy Jake finally opened it a tiny bit.

"All right, no need to knock the door down!" he huffed. "Whaddya want?"

Beardy Jake didn't look like he'd only just woken up; he looked like he hadn't gone to bed at all. His eyes were all puffy, wide and red, like a hamster with hay fever, only scarier and angrier.

"Err, you guys missed breakfast," I said, trying to sound cool while peering in through the crack. "Is Si in there too?"

"Nah."

"Oh. Where is he then?"

"Dunno."

"When did you last see him?"

"Yesterday."

"He didn't sleep here?"

"Nah."

And after those four one-word answers, Beardy Jake slammed his bedroom door shut again.

Nooooo, the situation was even worse than I had

expected. Not only were our centre backs still fighting, but Si was on the loose again. I checked with Hugo, but he hadn't seen him.

"He says there were five bread rolls missing from the kitchen this morning, though," Rafa translated for me.

OK, good, that sounded like Si. Hopefully, that meant he was still in the hotel. The Tigers split up and began searching every room, until eventually ...

"FOUND HIM!" Connor called out. "He's sleeping in the shed!"

Yes, there was Si, lying next to a rusty lawnmower, snoring loudly and covered in breadcrumbs. ***PHEW!*** At least he was safe and sound-ly asleep. Now that we'd found him, it was time for me to fix Si's friendship with Beardy Jake. Their fight had to be about something more than one bad football match. Maybe it was more of a roomie row?

Either way, it was easy to let "just a bit of beef" become a whole lot bigger at a tournament like the Worldies. With everyone together the whole time, there was nowhere to escape...

TING! LIGHT-BULB MOMENT! A-ha! I had an idea! After sending all the other Tigers away on a team trip to the local souvenir shop, I got to work.

"Don't worry, I've got an idea," I whispered to Tabia, followed by some top-secret instructions.

"Oh Johnny, you're a genius!" she shouted over her shoulder as she rushed off.

At first, Sleepy Si really didn't want to go back to his bedroom, so I lied and told him he just needed to pack his bag and then he'd be moving into his own room.

"Has it got a fan?" he asked, and I nodded. "OK, thanks. Let's go get my stuff."

When we arrived at the room formerly known as the Party Palace, I banged on the door until Beardy Jake opened up.

"Si's just here to pack his bag," I told him, but as soon as the two of them were in the same room together, ***CLICK! CLACK!*** Tabia quickly turned the spare key she'd taken from Hugo's office, locking our centre backs in the – dun dun duuuuuuun – "ONLY MATES CAN ESCAPE" ROOM!

"Hey, let me out!" Beardy Jake yelled, trying and trying to open the door from the inside, but his key wouldn't budge while our key was in the outside.

"No, let ME out!" Si argued back.

"We're not letting either of you out until you stop fighting and make friends again," I explained through the door. "The Tigers are a team and we all work together, so the sooner you start talking to each other the better."

At first, all we could hear were grunts and grumbles from the escape room, but eventually, Beardy Jake said some actual words:

"Look, mate, I'm sorry I got mad at you on the pitch yesterday. You know how much I hate losing, and that Mensah guy was making us look like FOOLS!"

"I'm sorry too, mate. One bad game doesn't make us bad defenders, innit."

"True that, mate," Beardy Jake agreed.

Just because they kept calling each other "mate" didn't mean they were, though. Was their friendship really fixed that easily? Surely their fight had to be about more than just the Bolgatanga match? I was still suspicious, and I was right to be because Si had more to say:

"Plus, I gotta be honest, mate, the whole us sharing a room thing was really startin' to stress me out, but it's all good now because I'm movin' to—"

"Wait, what you on about?!" Beardy Jake burst out, so mad that the "mate" bit was forgotten. "You loved the Party Palace idea just as much as me!"

"Not really, mate. I only went along with it because I'm new to the team. I liked the music part; just not the mess afterwards."

"What mess?"

"You probs didn't notice 'coz I always cleared it up after you went to sleep."

"Oh," Beardy Jake muttered, trying to work out whether to a) keep battling or b) back down. In the end, he went for Option A (wrong choice). "Well, if we're opening up and 'fessing all our feelz, I ain't happy with the way you're actin'. I was the one who got you into this team in the first place, or did ya forget that? You come in late, nearly make us miss our flight, bang on about animal battles and now you think you're too good to hang out with me!"

CRASH! THUD! CLUNK! We could hear things being thrown around the room, things that sounded heavy and dangerous. Tabia gave me a look that said, *Maybe it was too soon to call you a genius, Johnny.* Uh-oh. This was starting to seem like my least amazing idea of all time. At this rate, the "Only Mates Can Escape" Room would have to stay locked for ever.

"Why would I wanna hang out with you when you keep makin' digs about how much I eat?"

"Oh, come on. That was just a bit of bantz after all those burgers at the airport!"

"It was only TWO," Si snarled, "and I even gave you a bit! Besides, I ain't the disgusting one."

"What's that supposed to mean?"

"You fart ALL THE TIME."

"DO NOT!"

"Yeah, you do though. In yer sleep. And you never ever say soz!"

"Why should I? It's natural gas, innit. Anyway, you snore well loud and your clothes stink of wee—"

"STOP!"

That was me, by the way. I'd heard more grown-up fights going on in the Tissbury Infants playground! It was time for me to step up and do my job – MANAGE things. Grandpa George was the best peacemaker I knew, so first I tried to be like him.

"Righty-tighty, that's enough pettifoggery from you two!" I shouted through the door.

"What?"

FAIL! I tried again, this time using less weird language:

"Look, it's great that you two are talking again, but now you need to calm down and LISTEN to each other. Well, to the sensible stuff, anyway. Beardy Jake, do you think maybe you could be a bit tidier, a bit less disgusting, and stop making fun of Si's eating?"

"I guess..."

"And Si, do you think maybe you could be a bit more focused on football than burgers, a bit less late for stuff, and start hanging out with Beardy Jake again?"

"I guess..."

"Good. Now we're getting somewhere! What's the magic word you need to say like you mean it?"

"Sorry, innit!" mumbled Si.

"So, can you let us out now?" Beardy Jake asked. "I mega need to fart but I can't in front of Si!"

"Not yet, no. You need to prove you're mates in order to escape – that's how this game show works. So, here's your challenge," I said, slipping a piece of paper and a pencil under the door. "The sooner you work them out by working together, the sooner you get to go to the toilet. Ready, set, GOOOOOO!"

Want to have a gooooo too? This is what was on that piece of paper. (For a big clue, turn back to p.87):

SOLVE THESE 3 ANAGRAMS (THAT'S A PUZZLE WHERE THE LETTERS ARE ALL IN THE WRONG ORDER, BY THE WAY)

a. PEE VILLAIN DENTS HOLES
b. SAAAAD CURRY BUBBLE
c. NAN SILLY GOON

"What the...?!" Beardy Jake groaned as he looked at all the scrambled letters. "We're gonna be here for DAAAAAAAYZ!"

Si, however, didn't sound so hopeless. He was on

to something. "Wait, we can do this, mate. I've got an idea but my spelling is spiky. You any good?"

"Any good?" said Jake. "You're talking to the 2018 Tissbury Primary School Spelling Champion, mate!"

I already knew that, of course. I remembered seeing his name on the wall in the school hall. That's why my "Only Mates Can Escape" challenge was so perfect. Because to solve the anagrams, they would need Beardy Jake's word skills combined with Si's interest in animal battles and his knowledge of the Worldies programme (another huge clue if you're playing along at home!).

"Soz, mate. I take back all the mean things I said about you earlier," Beardy Jake said as he scribbled away excitedly on the sheet. "You know your stuff about this tournament!"

"Thanks, mate. I'm soz too. I had no idea you were such a spelling superstar!"

"FINISHED!" they both cried out together, before sliding the sheet back under the door.

Are you ready for the answers? Well done if you worked them out like Beardy Jake and Si – they were all teams from Worldies Group A:

a) EDISONVILLE ELEPHANTS

b) BLUE BAY BARRACUDAS

c) LONGYAN LIONS

"Congratulations! You're mates and so you can escape!" I yelled out as I unlocked the bedroom door. At this point, I think I truly believed that I was presenting my own reality TV show. "Today's prize is ... freedom!"

"Sweet, so I can go fart now? It might be a poo, actually. I'm not sure any more."

Tabia shook her head and gave them an evil grin. "No, not just yet. There is ONE more thing..."

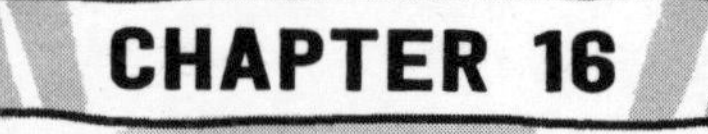

FACE PAINT, FREE KICKS AND FINALLY GOALS GALORE!

"Tigerz, we're really soz for the way we behaved against the Bears – it was bang out of order, and we totally let the team down," Beardy Jake announced at the start of the training session. "It won't happen again, we swear, and to show how soz we are, we've agreed to wear this fearsome Tiger face paint for the rest of the tournament."

"I quite like it actually," Si admitted. "It's a bit itchy, but it makes me feel properly fierce.

GRRRRRR!"

So much for Tabia's seriously mean team punishments! Never mind, the main thing was that Beardy Jake and Si were mates again, and, after their apology, all was forgiven. The Tigers were so happy to have their centre backs back that they even seemed to enjoy Mum's super-embarrassing Zumba class.

"...now wave those arms in the air like you just don't care. That's it, Hamza – shake those snake hips!"

"Boss, your mum is pure madness ..." a seriously sweaty, smiley Reggie panted, "but I love it!"

Wow, something weird was going on – everything was going to plan. The Tiger problems were magically disappearing and suddenly my to-fix list didn't look that long, ahead of our must-win match against the Alligators.

Team spirit? Sky-high!

Failed Tiger fitness tests? Zero! (Connor had a cut on his leg, but Dad said a minute of his magic spray would "definitely do the trick".)

Daniel was doing his shooting coach job (for once) by showing Rafa how to be a selfish striker,

Tabia was working on some awesome new attacking plays with the rest of the team and I was about to ask Coach Crawley all about his scouting trip to see the Alligators.

"Oh, what a great bunch of boys!" he told me enthusiastically. "They made me feel so welcome. Lots of singing and dancing, and they love their football, that's for sure!"

"I'm glad you had fun, Coach, but what did you LEARN about them?"

"Well, their manager, André Silva, is a lovely man and he speaks very good English. He told me all about Rio Alegre and life in Brazil. Did you know they have the only national flag in the world with a rhombus on it?"

"No, I didn't. That's super interesting, but what about football?"

"A-ha! Here's a good one – there's a Brazilian goalkeeper called Rogério Ceni who scored over

130 goals! Can you believe it? He took all of his team's penalties AND free kicks. Do you think we could try that with my Craig? He's got a big boot on him and—"

"I'll think about it," I lied. "Are you saying that the Alligators keeper takes their penalties and free kicks too?"

"Oh, I'm not sure, actually."

"Right, so what DID you learn about the Alligators as a football team then, Coach? You know, tactics, key players – that kind of thing."

"Sorry, JB, I was having such a nice time that I forgot to ask about all that."

Coach Crawley – a very friendly man, but an awful football scout.

Oh well, maybe it was better if we didn't know anything about our opponents anyway. "Focus on your own game first" – that was Number 1 in Paul Porterfield's "Top 5 Tips for Becoming a Totally Amazing Manager". In order to win and stay in the Worldies, the Tigers were going to have to be at their teamy, scoring-tons-of-goals best. And if they were, I knew we could beat anyone, even Brazilians.

🏆🏆🏆

WORLDIES MATCH 3:
TISSBURY TIGERS VS RIO ALEGRE ALLIGATORS

♫ *"Let's go, lovelies – eat those 'Gators alive!*
Get those goals guzzling out, miladdies!
We fight, we growl,
But we never mean to foul,
We're the Tigers, we're the Tigers!" ♫

We were all super fired-up for our must-win match, from the coaches to the subs-bench boy band to the two players wearing face paint. In fact, Beardy Jake and Si were so determined to show they were mates again that as soon as the game kicked off, they charged straight at the Alligators striker together, knocking him to the floor with an almighty "GRRRRRR!" ***FOUL!***

"Too much?" they asked, turning to their captain.

Temba nodded. "Yeah, too much. A little less passion please."

It turned out the Alligators keeper did take their free kicks, but luckily he was more like Craig than Rogério Ceni. After a really long run-up, he blasted the ball so high over the bar that it landed on the changing-room roof.

"Codswallop!" Grandpa George called out a little too loudly, but it was true – the Alligators really didn't look very Brazilian so far. Where was all the famous samba flair: the tricks, the flicks, the overhead kicks? Not at the Worldies, that's for sure. Instead, they had brought smiles, "sorry!'s and sportsmanship. No wonder Coach Crawley was such a fan; they were the friendliest football team ever!

The Tigers, on the other hand, didn't mind making enemies, and they were looking totally awesome in attack. Our build-up play was better than ever, but could we turn our neat touches into actual goals? Midway through the first half, Rafa played a one-two with Temba and then as he dribbled towards goal, a defender tripped him up. ***FOUL!***

Brilliant, because unlike the Alligators, we Tigers were the Kings of the Clever Free Kick! Word had spread around the Worldies about our Duck, Duck ... Shoot! against the Panthers, but don't worry, we had another nine incredible ideas to choose from!

"How many...?" was the one that Temba picked this time, which was short for:

"HOW MANY TIGERS DOES IT TAKE TO TAKE A FREE KICK?"

Perfect, one of my favourites! It all started with five Tigers stood around the ball, fighting over who was going to take the free kick: Reggie, Temba, Rafa, Hamza and Beardy Jake. They all refused to back down, so when the ref blew the whistle, not one, not two but all FIVE ran up at the same time.

Chaos, confusion, EPIC FREE-KICK FAIL! Well, that's what it looked like to the Alligators, but actually, it was all part of the plan. Because, as they walked away arguing over who would take the second attempt, the five Tigers had sneakily become four. Reggie, Temba, Rafa and Hamza were all there, but where was Beardy Jake? Creeping into the box unnoticed, that's where!

In a flash, Temba turned and chipped a high cross towards him, but wait, was it going to sail just over Beardy Jake's big, strong head? No, because Si was there to lift his mate up to meet it. ***THUD!***

GOOOOOOOOOOOOAAAAAAAAAALLLLLLLLLL!

"Cheers, mate. You're way better than Tyler really!" Beardy Jake boomed, this time lifting Si into the air as they celebrated. "1–0 to the Tigerz of Terror!"

Teammates working together – is there anything better? Anyway, back to our EPIC FREE-KICK WIN! I know managers are supposed to stay calm, but I couldn't help myself. "GRRRRRR!" I screamed as I raced along the touchline to join the Tigers. Not only were we winning, but on the pitch near by, the Bears were also beating the Panthers. Hooray, our Worldies adventure wasn't over yet!

It soon might have been, though, if it hadn't been for Rafa. As the match restarted, I shouted out all the silly football phrases I could think of:

SWITCH ON!
GET YOUR HEADS IN THE GAME!
KEEP IT TIGHT!
IF IN DOUBT, HOOF IT OUT!

But I was wasting my breath because the Tigers weren't listening. They were suffering from an illness I like to call ***WE'RE WINNING-ITIS.*** The symptoms are:

1) sloppy play (Finn passed the ball sideways like always, but forgot to put any power on it),
2) slow movement (instead of running towards Finn's rubbish pass, Aroon just stood still and waited for it to arrive),
3) silly decisions (when an Alligator rushed in, Aroon stupidly booted the ball all the way back to Craig without even looking, who stupidly picked it up – ***BACK PASS!***).

Brilliant, now the Alligators had another free kick and this time, it was INSIDE our penalty area! The striker flicked it back to their keeper, who ran up as if he was going to blast it high and hard again, but as the Tigers in the wall jumped up, instead he fired it low under their legs! (OK, so we weren't the only team with clever free-kick ideas.) The ball was flying towards our bottom corner, until out of nowhere, Rafa skidded across the goal like a penguin on an ice slide to save the day. Phew! What a hero!

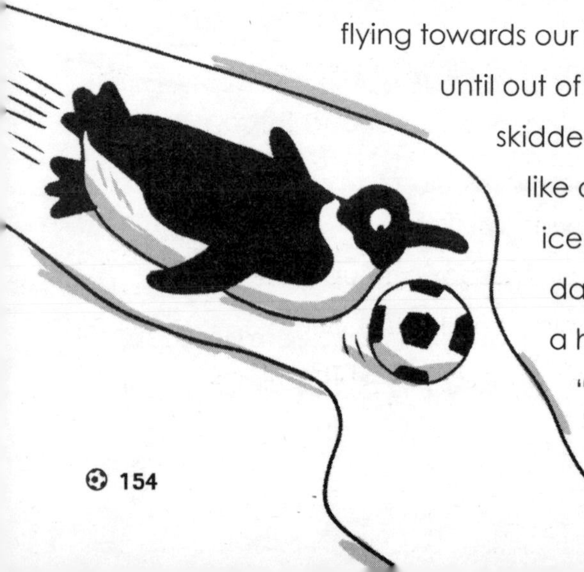

"Woah, thanks.

How did you know they were going to do that?" Reggie asked in amazement.

"I just heard them talking about it," Rafa said with a modest shrug. "They said they saw Capdevila do it on TV last night."

"Sweeeeeet! I swear you're like a language wizard or summat. So, you can speak Brazilian too?"

Rafa smiled. "No, they speak Portuguese, just like me."

"Oh, right. Actually, that makes sense 'coz there's one famous Ronaldo from Portugal and one from Brazil!"

Thankfully, after that Alligator warning and Reggie's language lesson, the Tigers recovered quickly from their ***WE'RE WINNING-ITIS***. They switched on at the back and zoomed forward on the attack. Because what's the best thing to do when you're 1–0 up? SCORE MORE GOALS!

Rafa flicked on Reggie's corner and Temba volleyed it in. 2–0!

Our front three were on fire!

Rafa was fouled in the box and up stepped Connor, our ice-cold penalty king. 3–0!

Woah, three goals in one game! The Tigers

weren't just winning; they were eating the Alligators alive! It was a bit like watching Brazil, actually. There was only one thing missing now: a goal for … RAFA! After creating two goals for his teammates, he was playing with total confidence. Nerves? What nerves? So, when Hamza's long-range rocket bounced back off the crossbar and landed at his feet, this time Rafa took his chance, and tremendously. 4–0!

At last, our striker had scored! I turned to give Daniel a great big "You're the best!" grin, but he was already hobbling off towards the gym. Oh well, nothing could spoil our perfect Worldies performance now; not my big brother in a bad mood, and not even a late Alligator goal. Because with the Bears beating the Panthers, the final group table looked like this (don't worry, I triple-checked my maths with Tabia first):

Position	Team	Played	Won	Drawn	Lost	Total
1	Bolgatanga Bears	3	3	0	0	9
2	Tissbury Tigers	3	1	1	1	4
3	Saint-Pierre Panthers	3	0	1	2	1
4	Rio Alegre Alligators	3	0	1	2	1

That's right. Despite everything, we had done it. We were through to the Worldies semi-finals!

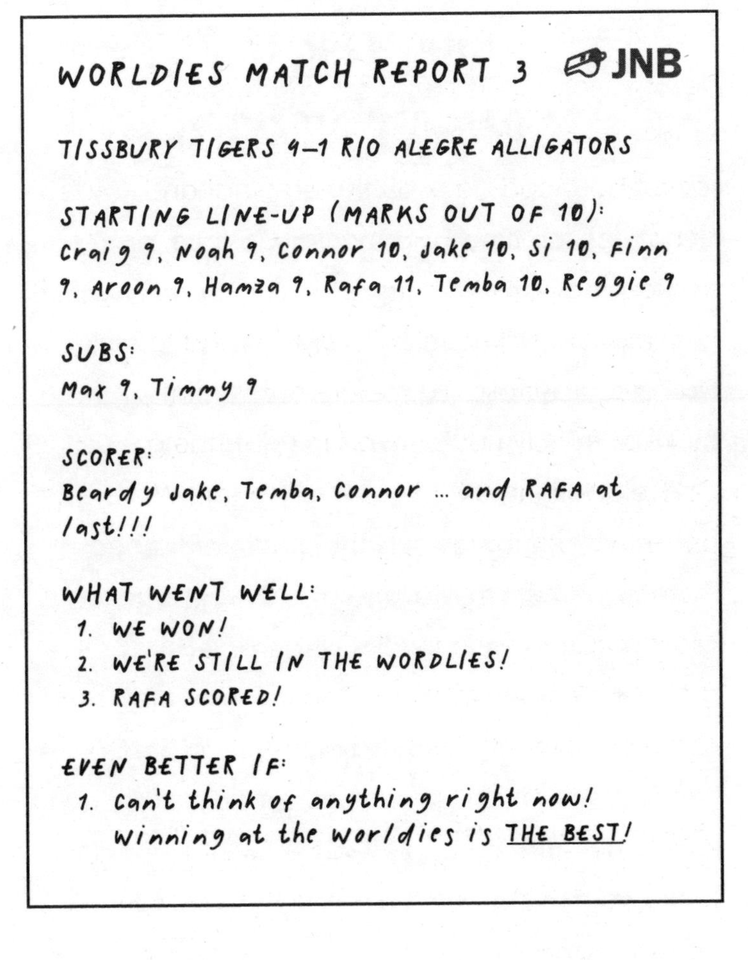
WORLDIES MATCH REPORT 3 JNB

TISSBURY TIGERS 4–1 RIO ALEGRE ALLIGATORS

STARTING LINE-UP (MARKS OUT OF 10):
Craig 9, Noah 9, Connor 10, Jake 10, Si 10, Finn 9, Aroon 9, Hamza 9, Rafa 11, Temba 10, Reggie 9

SUBS:
Max 9, Timmy 9

SCORER:
Beardy Jake, Temba, Connor ... and RAFA at last!!!

WHAT WENT WELL:
1. WE WON!
2. WE'RE STILL IN THE WORDLIES!
3. RAFA SCORED!

EVEN BETTER IF:
1. Can't think of anything right now! Winning at the worldies is THE BEST!

CHAPTER 17

A DAY-OFF DISASTER!

"Right, the ice creams are on me tonight. As many as you can eat, and with flakes!" Dad cheered, which, for him, was getting really carried away. But why not? It's not every day your favourite football team makes it through to the Worldies semi-finals!

HOORAAAAAAAAY!

And I had some even better news for the Tigers: "Tomorrow, we'll be training at... Only joking, team. You just earned yourself a well-deserved DAY OFF!"

HOORAAAAAAAAAY!

You see, we had an extra day's break before the Worldies semi-finals, so working on our top-secret tournament tactics could wait. But what would the Tigers want to do with their time-off? I wondered.

Sight-seeing?

Tapas tasting?

A stadium tour at Parc Vell?

Nope, none of those things.

"Guess what, guys!" Beardy Jake yelled. "The Party Palace is reopening tomorrow … AT THE BEACH!!"

HOORAAAAAAAAY!

I know, I know. It could have been way worse; they could have chosen three-legged rollerblading, or bullfighting. But still, I couldn't help feeling worried about the Tigers, with our Worldies semi-final coming up so soon. What if something went wrong at the beach, or in the sea? *What if? What if?* It was like all the *what ifs* in the world had ganged up together to take over my brain.

THINGS THAT COULD GO WRONG:

AT THE BEACH

1. SUNBURN
2. SUNSTROKE
3. GENERAL BEACH "BANTZ"
4. FRISBEE/VOLLEYBALL/BEACH FOOTBALL INJURY

IN THE SEA

1. JELLYFISH STING
2. SHARK BITE (ARE THERE SHARKS IN SPAIN?!)
3. GENERAL SEA "SILLIEZ"
4. DROWNING

Arghhhhh! Suddenly, I wished the Tigers had chosen bullfighting, after all.

"Dad, you know your huge football first-aid kit that filled up most of your suitcase?" I asked.

"Yes, son?"

"I need you to bring it all to the beach tomorrow please."

"What – even the fold-away stretcher?"

I nodded. "Even the oxygen tank, Dad."

🏆🏆🏆

"This spot'll do," Temba decided as team captain, throwing his bag down on the sand and spreading out his towel. Due to kid-at-Christmas levels of excitement, we had left Hotel Hugo super early that morning, and so the beach was still pretty empty.

"Good, 'coz I don't think I could carry this much further," Si spluttered. "This thing weighs a ton, Mr Ball!"

"Yeah, what have you got in here – a dead body?" panted Beardy Jake, who was carrying the other end.

"Only a few dead frogs," Dad replied. "For their healing powers, of course."

Suddenly, Beardy Jake and Si looked a little sick as well as sweaty, and they dropped the football first-aid kit in a hurry. They soon cheered up, though, once Reggie had set up the speakers and turned up the TUUUUUUNEZ. The Party Palace was officially open again!

Other than a few dirty looks from the locals and a few calls of "Could you please turn that down!" from Mum and Dad, our beach trip was all going well, until...

"Right, time for a swim," Reggie announced, taking off his T-shirt. "Last one in the sea's gotta sleep in Hugo's shed tonight!"

Oh no, DANGER ALERT: general beach "bantz", plus potential sunburn scenario!

"Dad!" I called out, but no, our Team Physio was fast asleep already. "Mum?"

"Woah, there. Not so fast, cowboys!" she shouted, pulling two sun-cream bottles out of the front pocket of her football folder holder and trying to spin them around her fingers like pistols.

"You'll be needing some of this on first, and then a thirty-minute sit-down to let it soak in properly."

GROAN!

Thanks, Mum. Sorry, Mum! I felt bad because I always gave her the boring, grown-up jobs, but at least that was one danger dodged. After half an hour of huffs and moans of "How much longer?", the Tigers were back on their feet and ready to race to the water.

On your marks, get set … ***GO!!***

Timmy's was the first belly to flop, followed by Temba's, then Rafa's, until, at last, Craig's made the thirteenth and final ***SPLASH!*** Max dived underwater and pulled his swim shorts down for being last in.

"Hey, not cool!" Craig complained, while everyone else laughed.

Uh-oh. The general sea "silliez" had started! Soon heads were being dunked, faces splashed and backs piggied all over the place.

Giddy up, Hamza!

Although I was really happy to see the Tigers having such a good time together, the manager part of my brain kept saying, *Beware! Hazard approaching!* Because, as Mum likes to say, "It's all fun and games until someone gets hurt."

The trouble started with Timmy. Remember way back at the Tigers team trial when Coach Crawley said he "certainly has his strengths"? Well, despite his best efforts, they didn't really include playing football and they definitely didn't include swimming either. He looked worse in the water than a camel in a duffel coat. Without realizing it, Timmy drifted further and further out of his depth and further and further out to sea, until…

HELP! HELP! HELP!

"Don't worry, I'll save you!" Temba yelled out like the most heroic team captain ever as he hurled himself through the waves, until…

ARGH! ARGH! ARGH!

No, he wasn't being attacked by a shark (they're mainly only seen to the south of Spain, in case you're wondering); it was a jellyfish. Well, actually not just one; a whole "smack of jellyfish" according to Temba, and he would know.

STING! STING! STING!

Somehow, he still managed to rescue Timmy and float him all the way back to the shore, before collapsing on the sand in agony. By the time I rushed over, his right leg was swelling up big time.

"Quick, someone do something!" I cried out, maybe being a bit over-dramatic. "Temba's dyin'!"

"COMING!" Dad called back, running along the beach in slow motion, not because he was trying to look cool, but because he had only just woken up and he was dragging his giant football first-aid kit behind him.

"Nah, he ain't dyin' – we've just gotta pee on him!"

It was Beardy Jake who said that. It sounded super weird and sick (in a bad way), but he kept going. "Trust me, I saw it on TV once. That's what you're supposed to do with a jellyfish sting, innit. So go on – he'd do it for you, mate!"

"Why me?" Reggie replied. "I can't – I just peed in the sea. Why don't you do it? You're vice captain."

Beardy Jake shook his head. "Soz, I'm empty too. Connor, you're penalty-taker, you do it!"

While "Pass the Pee" went on and on, fortunately my parents were doing more sensible and grown-up things. Well, one of them was anyway. Dad was magic-spraying Temba's leg and rubbing it with bits of dead frog, but Mum was asking the lifeguards for proper medical help (no offence, Dad!).

"Rafa, honey, I need you over here," she said. "What's Spanish for 'Excuse me, his leg really hurts!'?"

"*!Disculpe, le duele mucho la pierna!*" he replied straight away.

"Great, and 'jellyfish'?"

Rafa shrugged. "It's *'medusa'* in Portuguese, I think, so try that."

"What, like the woman with snakes in her hair from the Greek myths?" It seemed like Reggie was taking his language learning a lot more seriously than his roomie's jellyfish sting. "Oh wait, I gettit. 'Coz the legs are all wavy like her hair!"

"They're tentacles actually," Temba corrected him in between deep, painful breaths. "Not legs."

Thankfully, the lifeguards soon got to work, removing the bits of dead frog first, and then the jellyfish stingers.

OW! OW! OW!

Next, they bathed Temba's leg in really warm water. "See, that's instead of the wee," Beardy Jake boasted proudly, until Rafa burst his bubble.

"The lifeguard just said that sometimes silly – he used a ruder word, actually, but I won't repeat it – people try to pee on jellyfish stings, but it's a stupid idea and it never works."

"Oh, right," Beardy Jake replied. "My bad. Actually, maybe it was a comedy film I was watchin'..."

Anyway, that was the end of our disastrous day off at the beach. Mum took Temba back to Hotel Hugo in a taxi, and the rest of us had to walk the whole sweaty way back. It was waaay too hot to talk, so all I could do was think. That wasn't much fun, though, because the *what ifs* had teamed up with the *I knew its* to muddle my manager brain:

I knew something bad would happen at the beach!

What if Temba's leg doesn't get better in time for the semi-final?

I knew I should have booked the Parc Vell stadium tour instead!

What if that's the reason we lose and get knocked out of the Worldies?

Arghhh! First Daniel's injury, and now this. The Tiger captains were cursed!

CHAPTER 18

TIGER PLAN B: TOO MANY COACHES CAUSE CHAOS

"How's he doin', boss?"

All afternoon and evening, the Tigers kept asking about Temba, especially Timmy, who was feeling super bad about nearly drowning and needing to be saved. He even offered to donate his blood, which was a bit weird, seeing as Temba wasn't even bleeding.

It was great to see our strong team spirit, but by the tenth time they asked me, I was ready to scream, "I don't know, I'm not a doctor! I'm only nine-and-a-quarter-years old!" Don't worry, I didn't, though. Instead, I kept calm and repeated the same answer like a football manager robot: "He's recovering. We'll have to wait and see how he is in the morning."

The truth, however, was that Temba was definitely

a major injury doubt for the semi-final. When I went to visit him in his special resting room, his body was so covered in warm, white towels that he looked like an Egyptian mummy.

"Check this out – those tentacles have left a cool tattoo!" Temba showed me proudly, peeling back a few towels, but I could tell that deep down he wasn't feeling quite so positive. Although he said his leg didn't feel as stingy any more, it still looked really red and sore. Too red and sore to be playing in a Worldies semi-final, surely? Our captain was a real team player, though.

"What time's training tomorrow?" he asked as I left him to sleep.

"5p.m." I said. "But only if you're feeling bett—"

"Cool, I'll be there."

Temba did turn up for training the next day, but sadly he didn't last long. Four minutes thirteen seconds, to be exact. One misstep during Mum's Zumba class, and off he went, hopping away to the changing room, cursing under his breath.

"Sorry, Johnny. You guys are going to have to win the semi-final without me," he muttered miserably as he went past.

Poor Temba! Poor Tigers! Without our captain and key player, what chance did we have? I could hear Paul Porterfield in my head reciting his Top Tip Number 3 – "Never tinker with a winning team" – but now I had no choice but to change things. What we needed was a totally awesome Tiger Plan B, but I didn't have one. Yet.

THINK, JOHNNY. THINK!

BRAIN-BLANK.

THINK, JOHNNY. THINK!

Nope, still nothing. But I wasn't trying to win the Worldies on my own. Remember Number 5 in Paul Porterfield's "Top 5 Tips for Becoming a Totally Amazing Manager"? No? Well, luckily I do: "No manager is an island. To achieve great things, you must work together with those around you." So far, my team of coaches had been helpful (mostly), and now I needed all the help I could get. Maybe this was their moment to really shine? There was only one way to find out...

"Welcome to emergency coaches' meeting number two," I said, passing cold cans of iced tea around the table again. This time, though, my travel tactics board was as blank as my brain, except for three words followed by three question marks in the middle: ***TIGER PLAN B???***

"Thanks for coming. As you know, Temba is out of tomorrow's semi-final, so we're going to need to make some quick changes. If any of you have got any ideas, let me know and I'll add them to the mind map."

I was expecting at least a few minutes of silence as everyone did some thinking, but no, it was like I had opened a long-locked box and suddenly everyone's ideas were escaping:

4-4-2, 4-4-1-1, 3-5-2, 3-4-3, 5-2-1-2 (Dad's weird idea, in case you wondered) – there were so many different formations flying around that I was struggling to write them all down.

"Wow, thanks, everyone!" I said eventually, smiling but secretly starting to panic. Because what Paul Porterfield hadn't mentioned in his top tip was how to say, "Thanks, but no thanks!" in a way that wouldn't hurt my coaches' feelings. I did my best to be polite, but I couldn't please everyone. Actually, I couldn't please ANYONE, really.

"Thanks, Dad, but I think we need Beardy Jake at the back with Si, being big and strong together. At least for the first half."

"Fine, ignore me, but don't ask for my ideas next time!" he grumbled back.

"Thanks, Mum, but I think Hamza is best as a box-to-box midfielder, making late runs and firing long-range rockets."

"OK, luv. You're the manager," she said with a smug *You're making a big mistake* smile. "But if it was me, I would be wondering where the goals are going to come from."

"Thanks, Tabs, but I think Reggie is more of a

winger than a playmaker. His crossing is incredible, so we need him out wide."

"Suit yourself, ***SEWER-STINK!***" she shrugged.

"Thanks, Daniel, but I think Connor is at his best when he's legging it up the left. I know he's an ice-cold king from the penalty spot, but scoring from open play is different."

"Don't need to tell me dat, bro," he scowled. "Whateva."

Even Coach Crawley was a little less friendly than normal. "So, have you got any better ideas, then, JB?" he asked, and the other coaches backed him up with a big, loud "YEAH!"

It was a good question and the answer was, "Maybe", but first there was one more coach I wanted to hear from: Grandpa George. He had been strangely quiet so far.

"GRANDPA GEORGE?" I tried again a lot louder.

"Err, umm, yes, err ... sorry, what? I was nodding off bedward there," he croaked. It turned out he'd been snoozing all along.

"Grandpa, I was just wondering if you had any ideas about what we should do now that Temba is out of the semi-final?"

"Oh yes. Well, give me a jiffy – I'm still all in a zwodder… Rightio, I'm awakey-wakey! Now that young Rafferty has put the ballooning ball in the nodding net—"

"I think you mean Rafa, Grandpa."

"Yes, that's the yabadoo. Now that he has put the ballooning ball in the nodding net, I'd stick with him as our striker, move Reginald to the right and put Roderick on the left."

Who???

"Do you mean Hamza, Grandpa?"

"No."

"Max?"

"No."

"Connor?"

"Ah yes, that's the yabadoo. I knew it was an Irish name…"

At last, someone I could agree with! I guess great football minds always think alike, especially when they come from the same family.

"Thanks, Grandpa. I think you're right," I said. Sounds like a nice, simple sentence, doesn't it? But that's when the emergency coaches' meeting turned into total, everyone-talking-at-the-same-time chaos.

"Oh, right. So you'll listen to him, but not your own dad! Charming, that is. Is that all the thanks I get after everything I've done for you over the years?"

"Johnny-kins, I'm your mummy! I just want what's best for you and your team, and that's playing Hamza in attack."

"You do realize Reggie's right foot is only for standing on, ***FART-FACE?*** I don't think he's ever kicked a ball with it in his life!"

"It's certainly not my place to say you don't know what you're doing, JB, but..."

Arggh! I was under attack from all sides! But just when I was about to get childish and yell "La, la, la, I can't hear you!", Daniel said something that finally got my football brain buzzing:

"How many times have I gotta tell ya, bro? Rafa ain't a real striker!"

TING! LIGHT-BULB MOMENT! Maybe my brother was right, but not in the "I don't want anyone to steal my starlight" way he meant it. Because what if, rather than being a REAL Number 9, we turned Rafa into a FALSE 9 instead? Someone who *seemed* like a striker, but actually played all over the pitch, making him super hard to mark. Like Sergi Cortina,

Capdevila's captain and greatest goalscorer ever. Yes, an amazing idea was forming in my football brain... After all, what was it Grandpa George had said way back after our first group game? "When in Spain, do as the Spainish do"!

FALSE 9 BEATS "OFFSIDE!" TRAP ... IN THE END

WORLDIES SEMI-FINAL:

TISSBURY TIGERS VS LONGYAN LIONS

"It's the big one today, lads – tigers versus lions. You never answered last time, T – who wins?" Si asked in between bites at breakfast. The whole table went silent while we waited for Temba's answer. Suddenly, it was as if our semi-final hopes rested on a real animal battle.

"It does depend a bit on size, age and subspecies, but if we're talking one v. one..."

"Come on, T, don't leave us hangin' – just tell us!"

"...then tigers are better fighters, so they should win every time."

HOORAAAAAAY!

Yeah, we're gonna smash these Lions! Well done, captain! What a way to make the Tigers "GRRRRRR"!

Other injured players in his position (*COUGH* Daniel *COUGH*) might have stayed in bed, or stomped around in a bad mood, but not Temba. He was such a team player that he had even agreed to take Max's place in the subs-bench boy band.

"Let's do a new song today – ♫ *'The Worldies Final Countdown'* ♫?"

"Yeah, awesome idea!" Timmy agreed. Even though Temba had already forgiven him for the jellyfish attack, Timmy was still super eager to please.

With so much strong, teamy spirit all around me, even I, Johnny Ball: Tissbury Tigers manager, was feeling not-so-nervous about the Worldies semi-final ahead of us. Yeah, we could actually win this! Even without Temba, we still had plenty of the other two "T"s: talent and togetherness. Plus, our early-morning emergency team tactics meeting had been totally problem-free. It turned out Rafa already knew all about being a false Number 9, Reggie liked the idea of cutting in from the right, Connor was looking forward to playing further forward and Max didn't mind moving to defence.

"Just as long as I don't get LEFT BACK at the hotel!" he joked. "Geddit, guys?"

HAHAHA!

"Focus on your own game first" – DONE! What next, Paul Porterfield? Oh yeah. Top Tip Number 2 – "Work out your opponents' strengths and weaknesses". After his unsuccessful trip to see the Alligators, I hadn't bothered sending Coach Crawley to scout the Longyan Lions. Instead, I had done some last-minute learning myself just by looking at the Group A league table:

Position	Team	Played	Won	Drawn	Lost	Goals Scored	Goals Conceded	Total
1	Longyan Lions	3	2	1	0	2	0	7

It didn't take a football genius to work out their major strength – defending. The Lions hadn't conceded a single goal all Worldies!

And it didn't take a football genius to work out their major weakness either – attacking. Two goals in three games – even my shot-shy Tigers had managed to score six.

That was useful info, but it couldn't be taken too far, as you'll know if you've read as far as Paul Porterfield's Top Tip Number 4: "Never judge a team by the league table." Because maybe their keeper had played the three best games of his life, and maybe their strikers had just been super unlucky so far. We didn't know, and so we would just have to be ready for whatever kind of team the Lions turned out to be.

Well organized – that's the kind of team they turned out to be. WOW-ingly well organized.

"OFFSIDE!"

The Lions set their first trap in the third minute of the match and what a sight it was. The Tigers stopped and stared as all four defenders took one step forward at exactly the same second and then all threw their right arms in the air at the same time.

"Woah, how'd they do that?" Si asked Beardy Jake as if it was a magic trick, and maybe it was. Because how else could they manage to stay in such a straight line – invisible string? They moved together as if they were attached, like the players in table football.

So, which team tactic was going to win – our false 9 or their offside trap?

Rafa dropped deep, turned and threaded a perfect pass through to Reggie…

"OFFSIDE!"

Rafa dribbled from right to left and then chipped the ball over the top for Connor to chase…

"OFFSIDE!"

We had a special commentator for the Worldies semi-finals and finals, and how did she sum up the first half? *"It's been a tense stalemate so far with both teams cancelling each other out. Let's hope for more goalscoring chances as the game goes on…"*

But really, that was just a nicer and more exciting way of saying, "It's been an absolute snore-fest so far with zero action. If things don't get better soon, I'm going to fall asleep like that grandpa over there!"

OK, so the Tigers weren't exactly thrilling the Worldies crowd, but, looking on the bright side, at least we weren't losing. And there was still plenty of time left to find an amazing way to beat the Lions' offside trap.

Think, Johnny! Think!

I tried, I really did, but it was hard when all I could hear was my coaches telling me what to do. Well, two in particular:

"When things go wrong, HOOF the ball long. Time for a target man if you ask me."

But I didn't ask you, Dad! I thought but managed not to say.

"I'm sorry, Johnny-kins, but this fake forward trick of yours just isn't working. Go on, gorgeous – give Hamza a go in attack."

"Mum, I'M the manager – not you!" I mumbled quietly under my breath.

Argghh! Why had I ever asked them for help? What a major mistake! Paul Porterfield needed to add an extra bit to Top Tip Number 5 – "...work together with those around you ... UNLESS THEY'RE YOUR FOOTBALL-KNOW-IT-ALL PARENTS".

I was expecting Tabia to join in with the "You don't know what you're doing", but, instead, she whispered, "Super-fast secret manager meeting?" and then walked away to wait for me by the corner flag. Here's a top tip of my own – get yourself a best friend (and assistant manager) who knows when you're about to explode.

"Look, ***MOP-MOUTH***, I'm only going to say this once, OK? You were right, and I was wrong about the front three," Tabs blurted out like it tasted bad. "There! I guess I should have trusted a football genius like you."

"Really?" I said in shock. "But so far, it's been a total false 9 fail!"

"Yeah, but you can't give up yet – it's only half-time. Believe in yourself, ***BUMPER-BUTT!*** Stop worrying and start working on a way for us to win. The Lions are catching us offside every time, so what can we do to avoid that?"

"Not run offside?"

"Good, but we still need to score a goal, so how do we do that?"

"Pass and dribble around the Lions?" As you can tell, my football brain definitely wasn't buzzing yet.

"OK, but their defenders can tackle as well as trap, so what else?"

"Shoot from further out, from IN FRONT of the Lions defence?"

"Now you're thinking! And who's good at shooting from far out?"

"Hamza, our box-to-boxer!"

"Yeah, and who else?"

"Well, Reggie scored that fantastic free kick against the Panthers..."

"Yeah, and who else?"

"Beardy Jake likes to think he can blast the ball, but—"

"Nah, who else?"

After a few seconds, she got impatient and answered her own question: "RAFA, duh!"

"Really? I'm not so sure, Tabs – he seems pretty scared of shooting."

"Yeah, but remember what Rafa was like at the team trial and at every single training session since? Back-of-the-net brilliant! You just need to boost his confidence, so he can do it in a proper match too."

Tabs was right: Rafa had the ball skills, but what was missing was the self-belief.

While my assistant manager talked to the rest of the Tigers, I spoke to Rafa about our plan for the second half.

"So, you want me to shoot? From far away?"

"That's right!" I said but it did sound a bit silly when Rafa put it like that, so I added some extra detail. "You see, when you drop deep and get the ball, the Lions will be expecting you to pass or dribble like you did in the first half. What they won't be expecting you to do is curl a shot into the top corner."

"Yes, OK, I understand."

Rafa didn't sound confident about the plan, though, so it was time for my positivity boost: "I know you can do it because ... don't tell the others, but you're the best player on the pitch!"

"Really?"

"Yes, really! You're a superstar and it's time to show it."

"Thanks, boss. I'll do my best!"

As the second half kicked off, Rafa's smile was even wider than usual. Hooray, he was all set to become a Worldies hero! With his first touch, he turned away from his marker, and with his second – ***BANG!*** – he sent the ball spinning and swerving towards the top corner. The shot caught the Lions keeper completely by surprise and sailed over his upstretched arms. Now, it just needed to dip down a little bit lower ... but no, ***CROSSBAR AND OVER!***

"So close – keep shooting, Tigers!" I shouted. But sadly, that was the first of many near misses.

Hamza's long-range rocket was flying into the net, but no, ***POST AND OUT!***

Rafa aimed for the bottom corner, but his shot deflected off a defender and into the keeper's arms. ***SAVED!***

Beardy Jake jumped highest in the box and headed the ball in, but the referee blew his whistle for an imaginary foul. ***NO GOAL!***

Rafa faked to shoot, but this time, dribbled into the box instead. After weaving past two defenders, a third tripped him up. ***NO PENALTY!***

"HOW IS THAT NOT A FOUL?!!" I yelled, but it was no use. Luck was definitely on the Lions' side, and so it seemed was the referee.

As the minutes ticked by without a Tigers goal, the "helpful" comments from my coaches started up again:

"Time for a target man, son?"

"Johnny-petal, you mustn't leave it too late to make a change!"

"Thanks, but no – RAFA'S GOT THIS," I said really loudly, hoping that he would hear too. Tabs was right: I needed to believe in myself AND my false 9.

Rafa must have heard me because, straight

away, he puffed out his chest and charged over to the right. When Aroon's pass arrived, Rafa flicked the ball first-time to Reggie and carried on running into the middle, calling for the...

"*UM-DOIS!*"

"Comin' up, Ronaldo!" Reggie replied proudly as he passed the ball back for the Portuguese "one-two".

Rafa was on the edge of the "D" now, with enough space and time to steady himself and pick his spot. This was it, his hero-making moment. ***BANG!*** The ball flew past the Lions keeper before he could even lift his gloves up. 1–0!

GOOOOOOOOOOOAAAAAAAAAALLLLLLLLL!

Rafa to the rescue! At last, our false 9 had beaten the Lions' offside trap and the Tigers were now only moments away from reaching the Worldies final! I was desperate to run over and give Rafa a great big hero's hug, but first, I had a bestie to thank.

"Thanks for believing in me, Tabs – what would I do without you?" I said, doing our secret handshake.

"You're welcome, ***NAPPY-NOSE***. Oh, and the answer is LOSE!"

Five minutes – that was all that was left of the match. Five minutes flies by in a flash when you're having fun, but when you're defending a 1–0 lead in a Worldies semi-final? Trust me, it feels like FOR EVER! But with Timmy replacing Finn as our annoying eager beaver in midfield, the Tigers fought off the Lions all the way to the end.

FWEEET!

At the final whistle, the pitch looked more like a battlefield. Some players fell to their knees, others face-planted on the grass, and others sat with their head between their legs in the "I'm disappointed and/or going to be sick" position. There were exhausted, emotional bodies everywhere. I mean, I was just the Tissbury manager; I hadn't played a single minute, but I still felt like I'd run a marathon.

Football, eh? What a beautiful game it is, especially when your team is through to the Worldies final!

"TIGERZ!"

WORLDIES MATCH REPORT 4 JNB

TISSBURY TIGERS 1–0 LONGYAN LIONS

STARTING LINE-UP (MARKS OUT OF 10):
Craig 10, Noah 10, Max 10, Jake 10, Si 10, Finn 10, Aroon 10, Hamza 10, Reggie 10, Rafa 11, Connor 10

SUBS:
Timmy 10

SCORER:
Rafa to the rescue!!!!

WHAT WENT WELL:

1. WE WON, even without our captain, Temba!
2. WE'RE IN THE WORDLIES FINAL!!!
3. Rafa finally showed what a superstar he is.
4. Tabs reminded me what an awesome assistant manager she is.

EVEN BETTER IF:

1. Mum and Dad weren't such football-know-it-all parents
2. Temba is back and fit to play in the final. Fingers crossed!

CHAPTER 20

FOOD, THEN A FAMILY FIGHT, THEN A FAMILY FOOD FIGHT

♫ *"Don't stop believin',*

We Tigerz got that winning feelin',

Worldies, final,

We go on and on and on and on…" ♫

In the changing rooms and on the way to Hotel Hugo, the Tigers didn't stop singing either, not even for a second. What an achievement! We felt on top of the Worldies already, even if we hadn't won the trophy just yet.

"This calls for a celebration dinner tonight!" Dad cried out. "Oh, but I can't seem to find my wallet. Chris?"

Coach Crawley was, of course, too friendly to say no. "Sure, my treat, Tigers!"

HOORAAAAAAY!!!

Hugo kindly recommended a restaurant called

"Café Clive", but, based on the name and the state of his hotel, we decided that might be a bad idea.

"Why don't you choose where we go, Rafa?" Tabia suggested. "You won us the game, plus you know what all the words mean."

Excellent idea, Assistant Manager! Why hadn't I thought of that? Because I was giving my brain a well-earned break, that's why, and giving Tabia the chance to take charge.

After walking straight past "Café Clive" – which had a sign in the window saying, "2 4 1 Bacon Baps" – Rafa picked "Casa de Comida", which looked waaay better and waaay more Spanish.

"Right, let's get this celebration dinner started!" Si said, rubbing his hands greedily. "I'm starvin'. Do they do burgers, Rafa?"

"They do EVERYTHING – it's called 'House of Food' for a reason!"

HOORAAAAAAY!!!

An hour and many mouthfuls of muy tasty comida later, the Tigers looked sleepy and no longer starvin'.

"Hey, boss. So do we get another day off tomorrow?" Beardy Jake asked, leaning back in his chair and letting out a big ***BELCH!***

"Yes, you'll have a lie-in..."

HOORAAAAAAAY!!!

"...but then I've booked a super-special activity for us all in the afternoon..."

OHHHHHHHHHH!

To be fair, that didn't sound very exciting, but wait until they heard what it was: "...A STADIUM TOUR AT PARC VELL!"

HOORAAAAAAAY!!!

"Thanks, Johnny!" Temba shouted from the other end of the table. "This way, we can make ourselves at home before the big final, boys!"

HOORAAAAAAAY!!!

As I suspected, it was going to take more than a sore, stingy leg to keep our captain away from the Parc Vell pitch. It was Temba's dream to play there and he was determined to lead his team to Worldies glory.

Everyone was enjoying themselves, except for one grumpy-guts. Yep, you guessed it – Daniel. My brother hadn't said a word all through dinner; instead, he'd just sat there with a frowny face like his team had lost. But they hadn't; they'd won a Worldies semi-final! I know it must have been hard watching the Tigers do well without him, but couldn't he at least pretend to be happy for them? Nope. At the final whistle, I had gone over to say "Thanks!" for helping Rafa, and his reply?

"You got lucky, bro, and so did he. A false-9 fluke – that's what that woz."

Despite my brother's bad mood, the winning feeling was still there when I went to bed that night. But as soon as I woke up the next morning, it was gone; instead, the nerves had kicked in like a waterfall to the face. Argggghhh!

We were about to play in the Worldies final, at Parc Vell, in front of thousands of fans, on the same pitch as superstars like Sergi Cortina! ***GULP!*** What if I made the stupidest mistake of my manager life? What if I messed everything up and we lost because of me? What if I forgot something super important like my notebook, or my shorts, or the rules of football?

All those *what ifs* were already super-stressing me out, so the last thing I needed was a breakfast "chat" with just Mum and Dad. But with everyone else having a long lie-in, that's exactly what I got. After a quick, "How did you sleep, snookums?", the conversation moved straight on to – surprise, surprise – football.

"Feeling good about the final, froggie? We're always here to help, you know."

"Thanks, but I don't really want to talk about it right now," I said, hoping that would be the end. But of course, it wasn't; it was just the beginning.

"What's wrong, sweetie-pie? Let's turn that frown upside down! You're doing so well, darling, and, with Temba back, you can put that fake-forward trick behind you."

I tried to keep my mouth shut, I really did, but the

words still came tumbling out. "Actually, we're going to stick with the false 9. With Temba back, it should work even better in the final."

Dad did a face that looked like he was in serious pain. "Oooo, are you sure about that, son? It didn't work very well in the semi-final if you ask me."

Again, I couldn't help myself. "Actually, that tactic was how we won the game," I argued back, but not angrily. Yet.

"Your father's right. Why don't we just keep things nice and simple for the final?"

We? WE?! "Thanks for your suggestions, but I want to think things through for myself," I said, sounding calm in my head at least.

But my parents weren't listening; they were lost in their own "better" ideas. Arghhh! Where was Tabia when I needed her? I was about to explode. If my parents said one more thing about—

"The Worldies – they've gone to your head, son. You think you're too much of a football genius to listen to your own family now? Well, you're going about this the wrong way if you ask me."

That was it! No more, Mr Nice Manager!

"BUT I DIDN'T ASK YOU, DAD!"

"Now, now, dumpling. I don't think—"

"MUM, I'M THE MANAGER, NOT YOU!"

That was when the Tigers all walked in for breakfast, right in the middle of our family bust-up. Seriously awkward timing. I could blame my lack of sleep or Hotel Hugo's roasting rooms, but really it was all about football. Like always.

"Johnny-wobble, where's all this coming from?" Mum whispered in her "Please don't cause a scene" voice. "We're only trying to help. We're your *parents* – and your coaches – but mainly your parents!"

Unlike Mum, I was having trouble finding my indoor voice. "YES, I KNOW, BUT I WANT TO DO THIS FOR MYSELF, WITHOUT YOU GUYS BUTTING IN AND TELLING ME WHAT TO DO ALL THE TIME!"

That was when Daniel hobbled in for breakfast. *Perfect*, I thought. Surely my moody teenage brother would understand about our football-know-it-all parents, and take my side in the family fight? But I thought wrong.

"Nah, you guys leave me outta this," he said, sitting down at the furthest-away table possible. "I ain't bovvered."

I know I shouldn't have been surprised, and I know I shouldn't have been upset, but I was. I WAS upset. I was exploding and my own brother didn't even want to know.

"WHY WON'T YOU HELP ME? I NEED SOME SUPPORT AND YOU'RE SUPPOSED TO BE A COACH, REMEMBER – AS WELL AS MY BIG BROTHER! SO, WHY CAN'T YOU JUST STICK UP FOR ME FOR ONCE?!"

Breathe, Johnny. Breathe!

"Bro, I did what you asked! I showed Rafa how to be a selfish striker and he scored a tap-in and a total fluke – job done, nuff said. I neva wanted to be one of your stupid sidekicks, anyways."

"OK, I know you're angry about being injured, but the Tigers are still your team too!"

"Nah, not any more. Once we get back home, I'm outta here. The Raptors wanna sign me up, innit."

Daniel was going to play for Rockley Raptors, Tissbury's biggest rivals? No way! That was a step too far. Suddenly, I was shouting horrible-but-true things, like: "YOU'RE JUST JEALOUS BECAUSE RAFA IS REALLY GOOD AND REALLY NICE, AND EVERYONE LIKES HIM MORE THAN YOU!"

SPLASH! Not water, but apple juice, and a full

glass right in my face. As I wiped my wet, sticky face with my sleeve, I looked around for things to throw back. A bowl seemed a bit dangerous, but the soggy cereal in it? Sure, why not? I grabbed two fistfuls and lobbed them at Daniel. ***SPLAT!*** My aim was pretty good, I must admit.

"You're gonna regret dat, bro!"

SPLASH! went a whole jug of milk, half over me and half over Mum and Dad.

"Hey, now that's not on, son!" shouted Dad.

"Daniel, we did not bring you up to behave like this!" cried Mum.

It wasn't just a battle between brothers any more; it was a full-on food fight. As I told you at the beginning: **My family + football = MAJOR FALL-OUTS!**

SPLAT! went the scrambled eggs, spoon by sloppy spoon.

SMASH! went bread rolls as hard as rocks, whizzing through the air.

The Battle at the Breakfast Buffet –

of all the crazy things football had made my family do, this had to be the craziest by far! The Tigers, meanwhile, were stood around watching and loving every minute of it, like fans at a football match. Max even grabbed a grapefruit and tried to join in, but one glare from Daniel told him we weren't joking around. The safer thing to do was to cheer us on from the sidelines.

FOOD FIGHT! FOOD FIGHT! FOOD FIGHT!

Fortunately, that was when Grandpa George walked in.

"Blimey jingles, that's enough brabbling for one breakfast!" he shouted, banging the ceiling with his walking stick. "What the gogglebox is going on?"

The four of us froze like guilty people in films: Daniel, with his arm held high, ready to launch another roll rock; Dad, with his fingers in the fruit bowl; Mum, snarling like a wolf with egg in her hair; and me, hiding behind my tray shield. What a scene, what a super-embarrassing scene! Thankfully, the pause gave us all time to cool down and think. Think, *WHAT IN THE WORLDIES ARE WE DOING?* Some of us were even supposed to be grown-ups!

Grandpa George, meanwhile, was busy grumbling about the lack of breakfast. "Where are all the blasted bread rolls? And the scrambled eggs – did you snaffle the lot again, Si?"

"Hey, it wasn't me this time. It was them!"

Si was pointing at us, of course. We had all dropped our weapons by then, but the evidence of our food fight was everywhere – all over the floor, the walls and all over us too. Grandpa George looked around the battle scene and sighed like he'd seen it all before.

"Right, Ball Brigade, you lot better scrub-a-dub-dub this place sharpish, or Hugo will HOOF us out of his hotel."

"Yes, Daddy. Sorry, Daddy," Mum said, becoming a kid all over again. "It was just..."

"Football," Grandpa George finished her sentence for her. "I know, noodle. I know."

PUMPED UP BY PARC VELL

The tidy-up took aaaages but by the end, Hugo's breakfast room was looking a bazillion times better than before. Mum even dusted the lampshades and ceiling for the first time in centuries.

"Talk about blowing away the cobwebs, eh, Ballies?" she said and then spent the next ten minutes laughing at her own joke.

It turns out cleaning is also a really good way to calm down after a family food fight. By the time I had finished scrub-a-dub-dubbing the scrambled egg out of the carpet, I was feeling super bad about everything – all the things I'd said and all the things I'd thrown. I was meant to be the Tigers team manager, bringing everyone together! It wasn't our proudest family moment and it certainly wasn't the ideal preparation for our Worldies final.

So, how could we fix things? Well, we could start

by making peace, not war. When our work was done, Daniel tried to sneak away, but Mum blocked the doorway and refused to budge.

"Now come on, lovelies. We're not leaving this room until we've all said sorry. I'll go first – I'm sorry, Johnny-buns, Mummy and Daddy – but especially Daddy – got a little carried away and cramped your manager style."

"Yes, sorry about all that, son. Football, eh? It won't happen again, we promise," Dad said (not for the first time).

I went next. "I'm sorry, Mum and Dad, for exploding like that and I'm sorry, Daniel, for shouting those horrible things. I'm feeling a bit anxious about the final."

Ah, that felt better and now we were just waiting for Daniel. After a long, stubborn silence, he finally gave in: "Soz, J, my bad about the juice, yeah? But you know what I'm like in the mornings."

It wasn't the best "Sorry" I'd ever heard, but still, apologies accepted, time to move on!

Before long, the Tigers had forgotten all about our family food fight too because they were entering the most magical place on Planet Earth – Parc Vell.

Wow, wow, wow – what a stadium! It was so super awesome that I've decided to describe it tour stop by tour stop:

1) The Start

"*Bienvenidos a Parc Vell. Me llamo Santi,*" our tour guide began. He was about to say it again in English, but Reggie's arm shot straight up like he was at school.

"Oooh, I know that first bit – it means 'Welcome', innit? And let me guess the second part – your name is Santi?"

"*Muy bien,*" our tour guide replied with a smile. "*Y tu nombre?*"

Those were new words for Reggie, who turned to Rafa. "What's he saying – something about my phone number?"

"No, I was asking, what's your name."

"Oh, right. It's Reggie. You speak English? Sweeeeeet! Let's go with that – waaaay easier."

2) The Changing Room

This is when the Tiger excitement really got going

because it was going to be ours for the Worldies final! It was probably about ten times bigger than our team changing room back in Tissbury, and ten times swankier too. Instead of uncomfy benches, they had separate, soft seats and, best of all, there were pictures of all the Capdevila players on the walls next to their shirt numbers.

"Woah! Check this place out!!!"

"Crossbar I'm sitting in Cortina's seat!"

"Nah. Rapidinho's MY favourite player!"

"Hey! I'M Number 4!"

Oh, and this is also when all the stupid questions started:

"Can I take a shower? I'm well sweaty!"

"Can I use the same toilet as Tammo de Spin? It's just a pee, I promise!"

"Can I open Leo Barba's locker and check if he's left any boots behind?"

"Can I sleep here tonight?"

Poor Santi had to be really patient, but his answer was always the same, in English AND Spanish: "No".

3) The Press Room

"Is this thing on?" Beardy Jake asked, tapping the big, fluffy microphone on the desk like they do on TV. "Testing, testing, 1, 2, 3. Cool, it works – quick, someone ask me a journalist question!"

"So, do you think Tissbury will win the Worldies final?"

"Think? No, I KNOW we'll win. We Tigers are gonna GRRRRRR!"

HOORAAAAAAY!

Phew, after getting things seriously wrong at breakfast, it was nice to be getting things right again. As I'd hoped, the Parc Vell tour wasn't making the players panicked about the final; no, it was getting them properly "pumped" for the big day. They couldn't wait to follow in the footsteps – and bum-prints – of their heroes.

4) The Trophy Room

"Woah, check out all that BLING!"

"Oi, Danny. Even you ain't got this many!"

"D'ya reckon these are all real, or fakes – in case someone steals 'em?"

"Don't even think about it, Max!"

The Capdevila trophy cabinet was even bigger than their changing room. It had to be, in order to show off all the cups and trophies they'd won. 217 in total according to Santi, and he should know.

"Hey, Johnny. So how many trophies have the Tigers got?"

Great question, Temba! Fortunately, I was expecting it; no, actually, I was hoping for it because the answer was pretty brilliant:

"Forty-nine. So if we win the final, we would reach the big fifty!"

HOORAAAAAAY!

The Tigers were going wild already, and I hadn't even finished:

"That's eighteen league titles, eighteen Tissbury summer tournaments..."

"Nah, come on. Those don't count – no one cares about them!"

"...nine county cups, four national cups and ZERO Worldies trophies."

GASP!

Good, that was the reaction I was looking for. "That's right, Tigers. We've never won the Worldies before, so WE can be the team that makes history!"

HOORAAAAAAAAAAAAAAAAAAAY!

If only the final could have kicked off right then. But no, the best part of the Parc Vell tour was still to come...

5) The Players' Tunnel

Even with an empty stadium, there was still a special atmosphere in the air as we lined up in the tunnel, Temba at the front and me at the back. Perhaps it was the ghosts of Capdevila past, I don't know, but something was definitely giving me goosebumps. One by one, the Tigers walked forward to do what every Capdevila player does: touch the ancient wooden sign that said,

"*Paso a paso, pase a pase, siempre con pasión.*"

You didn't need to speak Spanish like Rafa to know that one; you just had to be a football fan. "Step by step, pass by pass, always with passion" – it was the Capdevila club motto, and one of the most famous phrases in the game.

When it was my turn at last, I was expecting an electric shock or something, but, instead, I just got a splinter.

"OK, ready, *capitán*?" asked Santi.

Temba nodded and, after a deep breath, he led us out onto the most amazing part of all…

6) The Pitch!

Sorry if this sounds silly, but IT LOOKED HUMONGOUS! As if it would take hours to run from one side to the other. As if you'd need a robot rocket-boot to get the ball from one end to the other. As if you could somehow get lost in it, even though the grass was perfectly smooth.

"Woah!" was the only sound that came out of Tabia's wide-open mouth. Yes, in real life, Parc Vell was even more mega than it looked on TV. As we stood together, gazing in awe up at the four walls of blue and red seats above us, it felt more like being in a beautiful temple than a stadium. Surely this had to be heaven?

"One day," my best friend said eventually, quietly but confidently. "One day, this is going to be my football home."

As I said earlier, it takes a super-brave person to say no to Tabia Haddad.

She wasn't the only one who'd fallen under the stadium's spell. Even Reggie and Beardy Jake were left speechless. For a few seconds, before the stupid questions started again:

"Santi, can we have a quick kick-around now?"

"No."

"OK, what about one shot each?"

"No."

"Penalty shoot-out?"

"No."

"How about head tennis and if the ball touches the grass, it's game over?"

"No."

"Fine. I guess we'll just have to save our mad skillz for the game, then."

"*Sí.*"

Luckily, the Tigers didn't have long to wait; our Worldies final was only two sleeps away! And as we left Parc Vell that day (after nearly two hours in the club shop, of course), it couldn't come quickly enough. Visiting the home of our football heroes had left us all feeling almost invincible, including me. So what if I was only nine-and-a-quarter-years old and still pretty new to the manager game? So what if that morning, I had been throwing bread roll rocks at my family at the hotel breakfast buffet? If I'd brought my team this far, I could totally lead them to victory again and lift a famous trophy in front of thousands of fans.

"TIGERZ, TIGERZ, TIGERZ!"

What next? Well, I could tell you all about the next day's training session, our top-secret team tactics, the return of my pre-match nerves and my terrible night's sleep. But that's not really what you want to hear right now, is it? The build-up always gets boring after a while, and I don't want to be a fun-spoiler. So, let's skip ahead to the football event you've all been waiting for – the Worldies final!

WORLDIES FINAL, FIRST HALF: OPERATION ACTUALLY KEEP ADJO MENSAH QUIET THIS TIME

WORLDIES FINAL:

TISSBURY TIGERS VS BOLGATANGA BEARS (AGAIN!)

"These guys are definitely grizzlies," Si declared at breakfast on matchday morning. "But it's OK because we're big and fast too, boys. Tigers could win any animal battle, ain't that right, T?"

Our captain paused, torn between his nature knowledge and what was best for the team. "Well, I mean, if it was a sea fight against a blue whale..."

"Come on, T, don't be like that!"

"Sorry, you're right, Si – us Tigers can take on anyone!"

HOORAAAAAAY!

We already knew all about our opponents: the Bolgatanga Bears ... again! Yes, after thrashing us 3–1 in the group stage, they had then beaten the local favourites, the Capdevila Coyotes, in the other semi-final, thanks to another hat-trick from their star striker, Adjo Mensah. He was on ten goals for the tournament already!

"But we've got nothing to fear today," I told the Tigers when we arrived at Parc Vell for the second time, "because we're a totally different team now. Last time we played the Bears, Beardy Jake and Si had a big fight and look at them now – best mates with matching fearsome face paint."

GRRRRRRRR!

Mind out, Mensah. The Tigerz of Terror are coming for ya!

"Last time we played the Bears, Rafa mega-missed an open goal and look at him now – our fantastic false 9 and our Worldies top scorer."

HOORAAAAAAY!

"And, most importantly, last time we played the Bears, we didn't work together as one united pack of Tigers—"

"Actually, Johnny, the word for a group of tigers is a streak, or an ambush. 'Pack' is used for wolves. Sorry to interrupt, boss."

"No. Thanks, skipper. That's useful to know. Where was I? Oh yeah, last time we played the Bears, we didn't work together as one united AMBUSH of Tigers, did we? But look at us now – we're a proper team AND we've got Temba back!"

HOORAAAAAAY!

Once we entered the Capdevila changing room, however, that strong squad spirit tipped over into total chaos. Maybe my team talk had been a bit too much because the Tigers were now so pumped up that they'd actually popped! You know that moment in a game of musical chairs when the music suddenly stops? Well, it was like that, only with waaaay bigger kids. There were players running, shouting and shoving each other all over the place.

"Hey, I crossbarred Cortina's seat last time!"

"Come on, Connor, I'm Number 11, not you!"

"Soz, Si. I got 'ere first! Nooo, stop ticklin' me or I'll wet myself..."

"So what? We all love Rapidinho, mate! I ain't movin'."

Arggghhh! My team of teenagers had turned into toddlers again! What we all needed was some ... "QUIET TIME!"

I had to say it five times but, finally, the Tigers sat down and shut up.

"Look, I know you're all super excited about today, but we really need to calm down and focus on football now. Remember, we're here to win the Worldies, not sniff the seats of our heroes."

"Sorry about that, boss!" Max said with a guilty smile.

"And we're not going to win this final,"
I continued, "by behaving like wild animals."

"But we're Tigerz—"

"Yes, I know, Si, but you're not REAL tigers."

"Oh."

"I want us all to sit silently for a few minutes and think back to our unbelievable journey so far and then forward to the match ahead of us. What have we done well? What could we do even better in the final? Because, to beat the Bears, we'll need to be at our absolute best."

Amazingly, that actually worked. All around me, the Tigers got serious. Some closed their eyes, some stared down at the floor, Beardy Jake and Si put their heads together, but NO ONE SAID A WORD FOR FIVE WHOLE MINUTES! Maybe if this manager thing doesn't work out, I could become a teacher instead.

With the Tigers in a more chilled-out mood, I decided it was a good time to hit them with my big team news.

"I'm sure I don't need to tell you who the Bears' best player is, but here's a clue anyway: he scored a hat-trick against us a few days ago. Things didn't exactly go according to my plan last time, so I've been thinking about ways to improve. I'm calling this one ... OPERATION ACTUALLY KEEP ADJO MENSAH QUIET THIS TIME!"

That didn't get the "HOORAAAAAAAAY!" I was hoping for, but I guess it wasn't the catchiest name I've ever come up with.

"So, the first part of the new plan is super simple –

NO FIGHTING! You win together, you lose together. Remember, teammates make the dream ... gates open. Gottit?"

YES, BOSS!

"Good. Now, sorry, the second part of the new plan is a bit more complicated. You see, Adjo isn't a stand-up-front-and-wait kind of striker. He loves to roam free all over the pitch, so to stop that, I want a defensive midfielder to man-mark him out of the match. And today, I'm giving that seriously tricky and important job to the fastest, eager-beaver-est Tiger of them all ... TIMMY! Sorry, Finn, you'll be on the bench for the first half."

Timmy had certainly earned his starting spot. All those water bottles and cones carried, all those subs-bench boy band songs sung – what a dream team player! Plus, he had successfully annoyed Adjo in our first game against the Bears, so hopefully he could do it again in the final.

"Wow. Thanks, boss. I won't let you down!" he replied, with a smile on his face like he'd already won the Worldies.

Job done. Team news delivered. And after a few more minutes of the Tigers stretching and me stressing, there was a KNOCK! on our changing room door...

"Let's go, team," Temba clapped and cheered. "Tunnel time!"

The Bears looked a bit nervous as we waited to walk out, but not the Tigers. Oh no, after their day-trip stadium tour, they were acting like they'd been playing at Parc Vell for years. No big deal! One by one, they tapped the old sign and then got their game faces on.

GRRRRRRRRR! Sadly, the stadium wasn't sold out for the final, but 10,000 filled seats out of 90,000 ain't bad, right? Plus, fewer fans meant it was easier to hear our small but very loud group of coaches supporters.

"Gooooooooooooo ... TIGERS! Let's bake these boys in a big Bear tart!"

"Come on, lads – you've got unlimited ice cream waiting for you at the final whistle! But only if you win, of course..."

"Have these muggins on toast, miladdies!"

♫ *"Oh when the Tigers go growling on,*
Oh when the Tigers go growling on,
I want to be in that ambush,

When the Tigers go growling on, on, on!" ♫

♫ *"Don't stop believin',*
We Tigerz got that winning feelin'" ♫

♫ *"Johnny B's Tiger-striped army!"* ♫

♫ *"We're skilful, we score,*
We growl rather than roar,
We're (the) Tigers! We're (the) Tigers!" ♫

♫ *"Who ate all the Bears, who ate all the Bears?*
Those top Tigers, those top Tigers, they ate all the bears!" ♫

Thanks, subs-bench boy band. You're the best!

On the pitch, Temba gathered his players together for one final team huddle:

"Right, Tigerz. On three: 1, 2, 3..."

"TIGERZ!"

Meanwhile, on the sidelines, I took a super-quick sit-down in the Parc Vell dugouts. Sorry, I couldn't help it; they were so fancy they looked like the inside of a private jet, and I half expected someone to come along and ask me if I wanted anything to eat or drink. Ah, so this was the life of a top-level manager! I could definitely get used to those comfy seats, but don't worry, I didn't stay there long. I had a Worldies final to win and it was about to …

KICK-OFF!

Even with the big-match pressure on, the Tigers stuck to my game plan like they had superglue on their boots. They played together like the teamiest of teams, with Timmy buzzing around the Bears' best player like a super-irritating wasp. Brilliant! Everywhere that Adjo went, he went too – right, left, middle, back, forward, even over to the touchline for the drinks break.

"What are you, my shadow?" Adjo grumbled after a while.

Timmy nodded back eagerly. "Yes, actually, that's exactly what I am. Sorry not sorry!"

Sure, Timmy made a few fouls along the way, but what mattered was:

1) Adjo hadn't scored,

and

2) it was making him more and more frustrated.

The one time he managed to escape past Timmy, Adjo came face-to-scary-painted-face with the Tigerz of Terror duo, who were ready to "GGGRRRR!" Oh, and tackle him too, of course.

"Yeah!" Beardy Jake and Si yelled out, doing a double high-five.

And what about the Tigers' attack? you're probably wondering. Well, I've got to admit with all that fearsome defending to do, we weren't creating many chances of our own. Our box-to-boxer Hamza hadn't fired off a single long-range rocket, and Temba was the only player with a shot on target. Still, that was what the second half was for.

"It's half-time in the Worldies final here at Parc Vell and it's Tissbury Tigers 0, Bolgatanga Bears 0. A game of few WOWS and many POWS," the commentator said, summing up the action so far.

Or, as I prefer to put it, "Operation Actually Keep Adjo Mensah Quiet This Time – totally on track!"

Well done, Tigers!

But what now, Johnny. What now?

WORLDIES FINAL, SECOND HALF: WHAT WOULD PAUL PORTERFIELD DO?

As the players walked off the pitch and then down the tunnel, I still couldn't make up my manager mind about my half-time message:

1) "More of the same, Tigers!"

or

2) "Now we up our game, Tigers!"

???? Arggh! Which one would work best? To tinker or not to tinker – that was the seriously difficult question.

On the one hand, Operation Actually Keep Adjo Mensah Quiet This Time was still only half completed. Surely it would be best if Timmy could man-mark him out of the match for the second forty-five minutes too? But on the other hand, we couldn't just sit back and defend for ever. To win the Worldies, we were going to have to go for goal ourselves.

What did my team of coaches think?

"I say we should wait, JB," Coach Crawley suggested sensibly on the way to the changing room. "Let's get to sixty minutes, and then maybe we can see if anyone's got any great attacking ideas." ("Anyone" meaning me, of course!)

"Nooooo, now's the time for us to push forward for the win, Johnny," Tabia argued, "not to sit back and be SWEET-CHILLI CHICKENS (no offence, Mr Crawley)! There's so much space out there. If I was on the wing, I'd be trying to test those tired Bears defenders every time I got the ball."

After the Battle at the Breakfast Buffet, Mum and Dad somehow managed to stay silent on the subject of football for once, but I could tell what they were thinking:

Be brave, our boy. Be brave!

Half-time in the Worldies final – this was the biggest, most game-changing moment of my manager life so far. What should I do? What would Paul Porterfield do? Sadly, there was no top tip to cover this particular situation, but in the end, I decided that my hero would be half brave and go for a bit of both: "More of the same, Tigers AND now we up our game, Tigers!"

"Right, team. Fantastic first half, but we're switching to wing backs!" I called out in my most confident voice, as if that had been my plan all along. "Timmy, I still want you to man-mark Adjo Mensah, only you're going to do it as part of a back three with Beardy Jake and Si."

"Welcome to the Tigerz of Terror! Want some fearsome face paint Timmy?"

"Sure!'

"Noah and Connor, I need you to keep tracking back, but as soon as we get the ball, I want you whizzing up the wings on the counter-attack. Hamza, I'm really sorry to take you off, but in our new formation, there's no room for a box-to-boxer. You're a dream team player, so I know you'll understand. Finn, you're coming on to play alongside Aroon in midfield and keep things nice and safe and sideways in the centre. We're going 3-4-3 – gottit?"

"GOTTIT, BOSS!"

3-4-3 in a Worldies final – sounds pretty brave, right?

Mum must have thought so because she gave me her best "bursting with pride" squeal, and Dad gave me a "Well done, son!" pat on the back. I didn't feel brave, though. I felt so nervous that my knees were knocking together. What if this was the stupidest mistake of my manager life? What if I messed everything up and we lost because of me? Oh well, we would just have to find out in the...

SECOND HALF!

Luckily for the fans – and the commentator too – there were more WOWs than POWs after the break. Rafa made his favourite false-9 move and then flicked the ball on for Noah to race up the right wing. In his attacking excitement, he fizzed it in low and waaaay too hard towards Temba, but he somehow controlled the ball beautifully on his boot and then – ***BANG!*** – the keeper tipped his shot over the bar for our first corner of the final. Progress!

"More of the same, Tigers!" I clapped and cheered on the sidelines.

Unfortunately, we weren't the only ones looking more dangerous in the second half. The Bears had come back out determined to show that they were more than a one-boy team. That was the only problem with Operation Actually Keep Adjo Mensah Quiet This Time: it gave their other attackers extra time and space to get into the game. As a cross came into the box, Adjo made a dummy run to distract our defence, and their Number 10 snuck in between the Tigerz of Terror to score the first goal of the final. 1–0!

"Hey, I thought YOU were marking him!"

"No, I thought YOU were marking him!"

What a defensive disaster! OK, so this was it: the ultimate test of the Tigers' team spirit. Not only were we losing, but Beardy Jake and Si were arguing again. Apparently, they had forgotten the super-simple first part of my plan: "NO FIGHTING!" Was this the beginning of the end for our Worldies-winning dream?

No, because this time, Temba wasn't the only peacemaking Tiger out there. In a flash, half the players surrounded Beardy Jake and the other half surrounded Si, separating our battling centre backs. Then, after some calming words from Temba and Reggie, followed by twenty seconds of quiet time, the two team huddles joined together to form one reunited ambush of Tigers. Hooray!

Honestly, it was one of the most beautiful things I've ever seen on a football pitch, and probably my proudest moment as a football manager. No, I'm not crying. YOU are!

"...Right, 'Tigerz for the Trophy'. On three: 1, 2, 3..."

"TIGERZ FOR THE TROPHY!"

That was the only part of Temba's team talk I heard, but whatever else he said, it 100% worked because the players walked away with their focused game faces back on, and soon it was 1–1.

Our captain scored it, but really the goal was all about the false-9 brilliance that came before it. Rafa started the move himself, with a clever pass to Connor as he flew forward from left wing back. Then, instead of rushing straight into the box for the cross like the rest of his teammates, Rafa waited patiently for the perfect moment to...

"Yes!" he called out, sprinting into the space left behind on the edge of the penalty area. Three Bears defenders flung their big bodies to the ground in front of Rafa, thinking he was about to shoot, but instead, with a first touch of pure flair, Rafa flicked the ball through to Temba, who finished things off in style. 1–1!

GOOOOOOOAAAAAAAAALLLLLLLLLLL!!!

It was a team goal so great that even Daniel gave it a quick cool-kid nod of approval. Hmmm. Maybe Rafa wasn't a false-9 fluke, after all. Thanks to him, we Tigers were back in the game!

I allowed myself two quick air punches, then went back to keeping calm and not getting carried away. What next? I decided to take Coach Crawley's advice and make a sixtieth-minute substitution. Off went a really, really tired-looking Timmy and on came Max. Although he wasn't as fast or eager as Timmy, he could be just as annoying in different ways.

"What do you call a panda with no teeth? A gummy BEAR!"

"How do grizzlies stay cool in the summer? BEAR conditioning!"

"What are you, a comedian?" Adjo grumbled after a while.

"Actually, yes! Why, do you think I'm funny? I couldn't BEAR it if you said no!"

HAHAHAHAHAHAHA!

The end-to-end entertainment went on and on, but before either team could grab a Worldies-winning goal, the final whistle blew. Uh-oh. We were going into ...

EXTRA-TIME!

Argghh! What now? This was where I was supposed to save the day with a moment of game-changing genius, but we were out of subs and I was out of amazing football ideas.

Think, Johnny. Think!

Nope, nothing. So while Dad went around lifting up achy, crampy legs, I gave a super-fast team talk, which was basically,

"More of the same, Tigers!"

But after ninety minutes of end-to-end playing on the massive Parc Vell pitch, that wasn't really possible. Some of the Tigers could hardly walk, let alone run, and so our 3-4-3 had flattened into a 5-5 formation instead. We desperately needed extra-time inspiration, but what we got instead was:

AN EXTRA-TIME INJURY.

"Owwwwwwwww!" Reggie howled like a wolf as he rolled around clutching his left leg.

At last, Dad had something serious to deal with! He raced across with his giant first-aid kit and a serious "I'll sort this!" look on his face.

"Feeling better now?" he asked Reggie after a minute of magic-spraying.

"No."

"How about now?" he asked after strapping his leg up with super-tight tape.

"NO!"

Dad couldn't think of anything else to do, so he turned to me and gave me a thumbs up. "He's fine! Right, let's get you up and playing through the pain, as my old manager used to say—"

"What? No way, Mr B. I'm proper hurtin' here. I reckon it might be broken!"

"I think you'll find I'M the Team Physio, lad."

"Yeah, but it's MY leg!"

This went on for a while – Dad trying to help

Reggie back up, Reggie refusing his hand – until eventually, our left-winger got halfway up and then fell back down on the grass with a horrible ***CRUNCH!*** and an even louder "***OWWWWWWWWWWWWW!***"

Well done, Dad – now Reggie's Worldies really were over! Plus, we had already brought on our two subs, so the Tigers were down to ten players for the rest of the final. Or were we...?

Sorry, guys, to make this story as super exciting as possible, there's something I haven't told you yet. You see, although we had only been able to find thirteen fit, teenage Tiger players to take to the Worldies, the tournament rules said you were allowed squads of *sixteen*. And I had signed up three extras just in case: my badly injured brother, Daniel,

my best friend and assistant manager, Tabia,

and ...

ME!

I know, not necessarily the best selection of superstars, but better than no one, right? Anyway, all three of us were there on the sidelines, so which one should be the emergency sub?

"Well, it should be Daniel, of course!" Dad argued (of course). "No doubt about it – he's the Tigers captain and one of the best young players Tissbury has ever seen."

"Yeah, but I can't even—" My brother tried to speak for himself but our parents were back to butting in and not listening to anyone again.

"No, Danny-diddums still has a poorly shin. Johnny-poppet, you should play instead! You were super-duper when you came on in the County Cup final for your school team."

"Yeah, but that was—"

"Come on, Liz. Daniel can last a few minutes and his penalty record is perfect—"

"No, Steven, he can't 'last a few minutes'! Didn't you listen to a word the doctor s—"

I know, I know, I was shouting at my family again, but this time it was CONTROLLED shouting. Because this was MY team

and I believed in them, I believed in myself and I believed in my best friend. Not only was Tabia an awesome assistant manager, but she was also a fantastic footballer, far better than me. Plus, this was her dream. I knew what I needed to do:

"Tabs, get kitted up and then warmed up – you're coming on."

I've never seen my best friend beam so brightly. "You sure about this, ***STOAT-STENCH***?"

Nod.

"Double-sure?"

Double-nod.

"Awesome! Parc Vell pitch, here I come! Have I ever told you you're a football genius?"

"Yes, you have. Now prove it, please!"

My parents, meanwhile, were still trying to tell me what I should and shouldn't do.

"Leaving a player like Daniel on the bench at a moment like this? It's madness if you ask me!"

"Don't be a scaredy-shirt, Johnny-doodle – get out there and PLAY BALL!"

"MUM, DAD – STOP!"

But no, it wasn't me shouting this time...

"J's right. I ain't ready and Tabs has mad skillz,

innit. She's got this ... and J's got this too. You're a killer manager, bro."

It was Daniel! He was backing me up at last like a proper coach, and an actual brother. I didn't know what to say, and neither did Mum or Dad, so we all said nothing. Perfect! Play on!

As our new winger raced onto the pitch with a "GRRRRRRR!", the Bears players didn't say a word. Instead, they smiled at each other and sniggered behind their hands like little schoolboys. Good, they thought that Tabia was "just a girl". She would soon prove them wrong...

Or would she? Sadly, Tabia didn't turn out to be the instant super sub I was hoping she might be. In fact, five minutes of extra-time flew by before she even touched the ball and then, when she did, she took too long and a Bears defender tackled her straight away.

"So much for those MAD SKILLZ," I heard Dad mutter in my direction.

But before Tabia could show off a better second touch, the whistle blew again for half-time in extra-time. Already?! The Worldies final was flying by. I had just one last sixty-second drinks break to somehow inspire my team of seriously tired Tigers to victory and avoid the unbearable pain of a penalty shoot-out.

Think, Johnny. Think!

It was too late (and hot) for complicated tactics, so I kept my message super simple:

"Team, no matter what happens in these final fifteen minutes, you've all been incredible and I'm mega proud to be your manager. Let's give it one last push together. *Paso a paso, pase a pase, siempre con pasión*."

The sound of that famous phrase had a strange effect on the Tigers. One by one, they lifted their tired heads to look up and all around them for the first time in ages. Oh yeah, this *wasn't* Tissbury Rec any more; they were playing in front of fans at PARC VELL, just like their international football heroes!

That magical moment didn't give the Tigers their energy back, but it did give them a new determination to make the most of their big opportunity.

As Tabia walked back out onto the pitch for the second half, she definitely looked more confident, but I gave her a "You've got this!" nod just to make sure.

When Rafa turned and attacked the penalty area with less than five minutes to go, he could easily have given the ball to Temba on the right, but no, instead he played the pass that the Bears weren't expecting – to Tabia on the left.

You've got this!

This time, she wasn't going to waste her big moment by taking too long. No, with two speedy stepovers, Tabia danced straight past the first defender. *Olé!*

"May I present: MAD SKILLZ!" I wanted to yell at Dad, but there was no time for that because more big scary Bears were charging towards Tabia to win the ball back. But that's when she spotted Rafa making a really selfish striker's run into the six-yard box (thanks, Daniel!). ***PING! BANG!***

GOOOOOOOOOOAAAAAAAAAALLLLLLLLLL!

2–1 to the Tigers – comeback complete! The final wasn't finished yet, though. There were still four minutes of football to play, and we couldn't afford to get ***WE'RE WINNING-ITIS*** again!

"SWITCH ON!"

"GET YOUR HEADS IN THE GAME!"

"KEEP IT TIGHT!"

"IF IN DOUBT, HOOF IT OUT!"

I shouted all the silly football phrases I could think of, and this time my players paid attention. Noah and Connor went from wing backs back to full backs, the Tigerz of Terror stayed strong and together, Max stuck to Adjo like a "KICK ME" sign on someone's back, and Finn and Aroon kept things safe and sideways. What a team!

"Come on, time's up!" I shouted, jumping up and down on the spot like I really needed a wee. I stared and stared at the referee, trying to lift the whistle to his lips with my mind power, until, eventually ...

FWEEEEEET!

We had done it! Tissbury Tigers were the new CHAMPIONS OF THE WORLDIES! Tabia, our super sub, had saved the day, and I, Johnny Ball, was officially an INTERNATIONAL FOOTBALL GENIUS! Or so my players and coaches were suddenly shouting in both of my ears, anyway:

"Yessssss, we did it! You're the baddest boss in the bizness! The Party Palace is officially open again ... at Parc Vell!"

"What a Worldies Win, JB, and what an amazing manager you are!"

"Hip-hip-HOORAY, grasshopper! You've done a crackerjack job!"

"Nice one, J! Oh, and I ain't really goin' to the Raptors, by the way – I just said that coz I was ragin' at you."

"Thanks, ***BABOON-BUM*** – you're the best football genius in the Worldies!"

"Congratulations, son – you were right and we were wrong. Again! Can I buy you an extra-big ice cream to say sorry?"

"Thanks, everyone. I couldn't have done it without you!" In that incredible moment, I didn't know what to do, or who to hug first. But luckily, our Team Co-ordinator (aka Mum) quickly got us all organized:

"Right Tiger tots, form a long line in front of the fans. Maximilian, less clowning, and more getting on down-ing! Hamza, it's time to shake those snake hips again. Daddy, you're going to need both walking sticks for this Zumba victory dance. Ready, Reginald? 3, 2, 1 and ...

WORLDIES MATCH REPORT 5 JNB

TISSBURY TIGERS 2–1 BOLGATANGA BEARS

STARTING LINE-UP (MARKS OUT OF 10):
Craig 10, Noah 10, Connor 10, Jake 10, Si 10, Timmy 10, Aroon 10, Hamza 10, Temba 10, Rafa 10, Reggie 10

SUBS:
Finn 10, Max 10, Tabia 10

SCORER:
Temba, Rafa

WHAT WENT WELL:
EVERYTHING – WE'RE THE CHAMPIONS OF THE WORLDIES!

ABOUT THE AUTHOR

Matt Oldfield loves football. He loves playing football, watching football, reading about football, but most of all, he loves writing about football for kids. With his brother, Tom, he has written the bestselling Ultimate Football Heroes series of playground to pitch biographies. He won the *Telegraph* Children's Sports Book of the Year for *Unbelievable Football: The Most Incredible True Football Stories*.

JOHNNY BALL is Matt's first fiction series. The first book in the series – *Johnny Ball: Accidental Football Genius* – was shortlisted for the Children's Sports Book of the Year.